BEING ASSERTIVE

WAYS OF RESPECTING OTHERS
BUT NOT LETTING YOURSELF BE
WALKED ON
— ESPECIALLY FOR PARENTS.

by Michael and Terri Quinn

HANDBOOK FOR THE PARENT ASSERTIVENESS PROGRAMME

FAMILY CARING TRUST

FAMILY CARING TRUST

IS PARTICULARLY GRATEFUL TO

Barnardos

FOR THEIR GENEROUS CONTRIBUTION

TOWARDS THE DEVELOPMENT AND PRODUCTION

OF THIS BOOK AND PROGRAMME

Copyright c Family Caring Trust, 1992
ISBN 1 872253 06 7

Illustrations and design: Pauline McGrath
Typesetting: Cassidy Printers, Newry
Printing: Universities Press (Belfast)

CONTENTS

Page

HERE ARE SOME OF MY RIGHTS:

1. I have a right to be treated with respect, no matter what my age is, or my sex or sexuality, or class, or race, or work (paid or unpaid) - and regardless of any way in which I may be disabled.

2. I have a right to say 'no' - or 'yes', or 'I don't know', or 'I don't understand', or to say nothing at all.

3. I have a right to say what I feel.

4. I have the right to say what I think - and to change my mind and think differently in the future.

5. I have a right to state what I want or need or prefer, and to ask for it (though the answer may be 'no').

6. I have a right to be different from you in my feelings, ideas, wishes, tastes, needs, standards, values...

7. I have a right to hear criticisms of my behaviour at first hand - rather than have people talk about me behind my back.

8. I have a right to postpone making a decision until I have time to think.

9. I have a right to make decisions that may not meet with the approval of others - even to make mistakes.

10. I have a right to question or confront any person or system or custom that oppresses others.

11. I have a right to be involved in decisions made by my family, my church or association, or a public body, when these decisions affect me.

12. I have a right to enjoy living.

A. Do you agree that you have these rights? Which of them do you find most difficult to claim?

B. For each of these rights there are corresponding responsibilities, (e.g. for number one, if I have a right to be treated with respect, I have a responsibility to treat *others* with respect and even to stand up for people whose rights are not being respected). See if you can decide what the corresponding responsibility is in each case.

ABOUT THIS BOOK

It may come as a surprise..

'A course on assertiveness? I would have thought that was the last thing *you* needed!'

That was the reaction one woman got from her husband when she mentioned that she was going to attend one of the assertiveness courses linked with this book. Her husband went on to say that he thought she was assertive enough. What he probably meant, she explained, was that he saw her as being already a bit pushy and aggressive in standing up for her rights.

The idea that assertiveness has something to do with aggression is a common misunderstanding and an unfortunate one. Many men and women, for example, have great need of a course on assertiveness if only to unlearn aggressive habits and discover how to treat themselves and others with respect.

The content of this book, then, may come as a surprise to some of you. You will find a good deal of emphasis on positive assertive skills like giving compliments and encouraging. You will see assertiveness as a balanced, friendly, respectful approach that helps you to be direct and open in expressing yourself. And you will see that being assertive calls for a lot of patience and gentleness.

Zoning in on parents

Unlike most of the material on assertiveness, this book zones in on parents. Not exclusively, of course. There are many examples from the workplace and the wider community, but most of the examples come out of a family context. This has a number of advantages.

Firstly, a family context offers great opportunity for daily practice of the skills - we may not meet a lot of requests or demands or criticisms outside the home every day, but most of us meet all of these many times a day within the family. And regular practice is the key to success in becoming assertive.

Secondly, parents have special need for support in learning assertiveness. It is wonderful that children are so much more assertive today, that they speak up for themselves and claim their rights and will not let themselves be browbeaten or bullied as in the past. But parents have to learn to cope with this new freedom. They need skills to enable them to avoid reacting with aggression. And to enable them to stand up for their *own* rights and avoid being steamrolled, treated as doormats or disrespected. Children need to be helped to distinguish between being

assertive and being abusive - they urgently need the model, the limits, the caring correction, the encouragement and the security that assertive, respectful parents can provide.

This book, then, is as much about parenting as about being assertive. Our experience of testing the material out in different communities would seem to suggest that it complements our existing parenting courses, and can make them more effective.

Part of a course

The book is part of a seven-week, self-help course. It can be useful without the course, but the skills will be learnt more effectively when you are following a programmed structure in a small support-group of parents who understand the difficulties. For those who wish to follow the course, a Leader's Guide and a video cassette are available separately from Family Caring Trust.

It must be said, however, that, whether you read the book or do the course linked with it, it would not be realistic to expect to acquire these skills immediately. Unassertive thinking and behaviour are deeply ingrained in many of us and will not disappear overnight. The book may give you a sense of direction, but skill and confidence will only come with practice. In any case, it's not a good idea to aim too high. You'll never be a perfect parent. Settling for being 'good enough' will lessen your frustration and guilt.

Acknowledgements

The book, and the programme of which it is a part, would have been impossible but for the co-operation and input we received from a great many people. We would like to express our sincere thanks to Gabrielle Allman, Mary Canning, Peter Devlin, David Gamble, Lynda Irwin, Martin Kennedy, Philip Leonard, Finbarr Lynch, Catherine and Michael Molloy, Peig McManus and Joan Sreenan. Also to Bernie Magill, our secretary, who was so supportive at every stage of the programmes's development. And not least to our own children!

CHAPTER ONE: WHAT IT MEANS

Why doesn't she make a stand?

'Can I have some of that?'

Helena was just sitting down to a cup of tea with her friend when her son spoke.

'No, Damien, you've already had some.'

'I only had a little bit. And you had lots.'

Helena felt her heart sink. Her son often did this to her. He seemed to know when to move in and catch her off balance. He knew he wasn't allowed more cake, but he seemed to know that the threat of a tantrum in front of a neighbour could get him what he wanted.

Anything but that, thought Helena - I couldn't cope with the embarrassment.

'Oh, alright, just a small piece. But that's it now.'

Her friend wasn't actually impressed. Why doesn't she make a stand and stop giving in to him like that, she wondered. A pity, really.

She was right. Helena has not learnt to be assertive with Damien. In giving in to her son, not only is she is not helping him, but she is guaranteeing a great deal *more* stress for herself in the long run.

And as children get older, that stress can increase a great deal for parents who are not assertive. Let's look at an example with an older child.

Oh alright, just a small piece

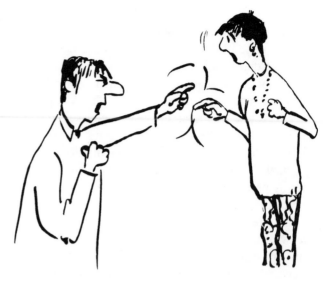

Get out! out! This minute......

The house no longer his own

Steven Ryan has come to the stage when he actually dreads coming home in the evening. It's as if his house is no longer his own. His fifteen year old daughter Linda has taken it over. Even if Linda's friends are not lounging around in the living-room, her music will be blaring through the house. This evening, her friends are not around, so, although he hates tension, he has decided he needs to talk about the situation.

'Linda,' he said, apologetically, 'I need to talk to you about the music..'

'What about it? she said, bristling and aggressive.

'Er.. The noise of it. It's so loud.'

'What do you know about my music? It's supposed to be loud! Just because *your* taste in music is so pathetic!'

He began to feel angry at being treated so dismissively, and his answer came back in a raised voice.

'Linda, I don't have to take that from you!

'Excuse me. *I* don't have to take this from *you*! Stay out of my life, would you!

Steven's eyes flashed with rage. Now he was shouting.

'Get out! Out! This minute! And don't come back until you're prepared to show some respect!'

'Okay, Mr Bully, if that's the way you want it! And maybe I won't come back.'

Three ways of not being assertive

Some people might applaud Steven for taking the reins in his hands and being assertive at last. But he was not being assertive; he was being aggressive. The two should not be confused. Indeed, a good way to begin to understand assertiveness is to begin by understanding what it is *not*.

But first a caution. **It is one thing to judge certain behaviour to be unassertive; this does not give us the right, however, to judge *individuals* on their behaviour.** For example, you may dislike people smoking in your presence, but in certain situations you may have your own good reasons for deciding to do nothing about it. In other words, you are making a choice and deciding what is assertive for you in that case. That is your right, and people would do wrong to judge you unassertive.

That said, here are three common ways of behaving that are not assertive:
- behaving in a *passive* way
- behaving in an *aggressive* way
- behaving in a *dishonest* way

Here is an illustration. The Thompsons are just sitting down to dinner when Keith protests:

'Yuk! Carrots! Disgusting!'

How does his mother respond?

Passive

Passive behaviour

The 'passive' response is to get up from the table, apologising: 'I'm sorry, Keith, I forgot. But don't worry, it'll only take a minute to heat up some beans.'

Those of you who are familiar with our Basic Parenting Programme will recognise this approach as that of the 'good parent'. 'Good parents' mean well. They often feel genuine compassion for their children and want to protect them from having to suffer. But, like Helena, in the first example above, they may be afraid of tension, or they may be so anxious to be liked that they will not claim their own rights. They can then let themselves be dictated to by their children - they can even become doormats to them and to others.

It's not just parents. Many people act in passive ways, particularly with their friends, neighbours and workmates. Because they are anxious to be liked, or to come across as 'reasonable', or because they are afraid of conflict or tension, they will often sacrifice their own rights. They will tend to agree with everything you say and they will find it difficult to say 'no' to extra demands. Anything for 'peace'! It's difficult for them to ask for or receive help. They'll begin with something like 'I'm very sorry to bother you..' They say 'sorry' a lot. Their body language is often apologetic too - a forced smile, hunched shoulders, lack of eye contact. They do not respect themselves.

Few people are so hopelessly oppressed and passive, of course, but a great many of us can probably identify with *some* of this behaviour. Most of us are probably quite assertive in some ways, but we may act in really passive ways in *certain* situations or with some individuals. Some of us, for example, may act in this passive manner when we are with people in authority - a boss, a head teacher - or someone who seems to know a lot more than we do, like a doctor or a mechanic. Sometimes, of course, that may be okay — provided we are *choosing* to act in this way. But the passive behaviour we are talking about here is not assertive because it is unfree.

Aggressive behaviour

A second way of behaving that is not assertive is the aggressive one. The aggressive response to Keith's complaint about the carrots is the opposite to the passive one. His parents act in

Just eat what's on your plate and shut up!

Aggressive

frustration and anger, speaking with raised voices, and in a scolding or threatening tone: 'I have to listen to enough complaining. Just eat what's on your plate and shut up!'

With the passive approach, people do not respect themselves, but with the aggressive approach they show little or no respect for *others*. When people act aggressively, they often adopt a tough, hostile attitude and try to bully others into doing what they want. They will not make themselves vulnerable, so they tend not to use the word 'I'. They'll say 'You'd better..' or 'You should..' rather than 'I need..' or 'I want..' They do stand up for their rights, but they tend not to respect the rights of others - they will often antagonise and hurt others even when they are fighting for someone else's rights. They may be bluntly honest with you about your mistakes, but they will neglect to compliment you or notice your strengths.

Now, it must be said that it can sometimes be quite appropriate - and assertive - to show anger. The aggressive approach that we are talking about here is the ingrained *habit* of ongoing bullying behaviour, tone of voice and body language. That is far from being assertive.

Sadly, many people who act quite passively, even slavishly, outside the home will often feel greater freedom to show their anger and aggression within the family. **It's almost as if the tension that builds up from all the grinning and agreeing with people outside the home causes them to lash out at the very ones they love most - their own children or partners.**

Dishonest behaviour

Thirdly, there is the dishonest approach. People who use this approach will often lie or manipulate, or pout and give you the silent treatment - anything but speak directly. They will often *pretend* to go along with things that upset them - but they will complain to others about you behind your back, and may even undermine you. They find it difficult to cope with constructive criticism, but you may find that they are extremely critical of others, often in petty, niggling ways. Instead of saying honestly how they feel, they may snipe at you ('Oh, forget it!'), or use sarcasm (Thanks a lot! You're really considerate, I must say. Don't worry about me, of course!'), or tell a little lie (They'll say 'I've a headache.' instead of 'I don't want to make love tonight.') If you forget their birthday, they won't come out openly and say 'Are you forgetting? - its my birthday. How are we going to celebrate?' No. They prefer to 'act the martyr' and leave you feeling guilty. They can actually be very good at manipulating people with guilt. In the situation above, where Keith is reacting to carrots, they may make everyone at the table suffer for the rest of the meal by speaking sarcastically - or in a self-pitying moan:

'Thanks a lot! After all the trouble I had preparing those carrots - that's all you have to say!'

Dishonest

Again, it must be said that we are talking here about rigid, unfree behaviour. In certain circumstances, there may be nothing at all unassertive about freely choosing to be 'economical with the truth' in making an excuse. It may be better to tell your mother not to visit next weekend because you are 'not free' than because the children don't like her!

Assertive

Assertive behaviour

The assertive approach is a fourth way of behaving - an alternative to behaviour that is passive, aggressive or dishonest. **It is an approach that helps you to be direct, honest and respectful in expressing your wants, needs, opinions and feelings.**

In the case above, where the child is refusing to eat carrots, Mum will look directly at Keith and say something like: 'Keith, I can't cater for everyone's taste. If you hate carrots don't eat them - but it annoys me when you talk to me like that.'

When people are acting assertively, they will usually respect both their own rights and the rights of others. Instead of sitting on the fence, they are not afraid to declare their hand, to say what they are thinking or feeling, or what they want or need or prefer. They will tend to use the word 'I' rather than 'you' ('I need..' or 'I prefer' rather than 'You need to..' or 'You just don't care!') Whether they are making a request or dealing with criticism, they tend to look directly at you when they speak, and there is no apology in their tone of voice or posture. They avoid padding in what they say ('I hope you don't mind me saying so, but..') When they have to give a correction or stand up for someone's rights, or say 'no', or accept a compliment, they tend to face up to things, and

you may notice that they can be quite at ease speaking directly and personally to you.

Few people measure up to this high standard, of course. We are all assertive to some extent and in certain circumstances. But the purpose of this book is to help us become more assertive, more respectful of our own rights and of the rights of others.

Four ways summed up

Here, then, is an example of how you might deal with a situation in each of the four ways:

Your friend comes to your house two or three times a week with two children and stays for hours. You understand that this friend is lonely, but you are not getting your own work done - and the house is generally left in a mess.

What might the *aggressive* response be? Something like: 'I've decided I'm fed up with you sponging on me - has it never occurred to you that I have *my* work to do?'

And the *passive* response? Perhaps: 'Come in. Come in. And how are the two little darlings this morning?'

What would the *dishonest* approach be? Maybe: 'Oh, I'm just going out to visit my mother. Why don't you come back another time?'

And the *assertive* approach? You would

Sharon, I'm not free at the moment......

9

probably avoid aggression by giving a direct, honest message. There is no 'right' way to express this, of course - that will depend on the situation and on your personality, but you might say something like: 'Sharon, I'm not free at the moment. I have a lot of work to catch up on this morning. But I do need to talk to you about your visits. I wonder when we could have a chat - perhaps when the children are in bed, so that we can talk without interruption?'

That allows time to deal with the issue respectfully, and with least upset to the friend. What is said when you meet will also depend on many different factors, including the kind of friendship you want to have in future. The 'chat' can be direct but friendly, and may involve some negotiation. In this book, you will meet a number of different skills that enable you to treat yourself and others with respect in these ways. For respect is the key to being assertive.

But my own way works!

A common objection to taking a more assertive approach is that the way you have been dealing with a situation has worked okay for a long time. Why risk rocking the boat? Maybe you shout and bully the children a bit, but don't they need that? - you've tried the 'softly-softly' approach with them and they just ignored you!

There is a certain logic in this argument. The truth is that aggressive behaviour often *does* produce immediate results. Children who ignore pleas for help with the housework will often jump to attention when someone roars at them. But does that justify using disrespectful behaviour? Besides, the effect is not lasting. **Shouting at people does little for developing their sense of responsibility - in the long run it usually only teaches them to shout back.** The answer, obviously, is neither in the aggressive approach *nor* in the 'softly softly' one.

A better way

Becoming assertive, rather, is an opportunity to unlearn the aggressive habits that we may have developed over many years. And equally to put to one side the fears and cautions that cripple us and leave us passive and unfree in so many of our relationships. It is an approach that enables us to communicate directly and openly and to act in a more relaxed and confident way because it is founded on healthy self-respect and a respect for others. It is particularly valuable for parents. For acting in this way introduces clearer limits, better communication, and a deeper level of respect within a family, and it is an excellent way of enabling you to *develop* positive qualities and values in your children - values like intimacy, affection, understanding, respect and appreciation. Few things can be so well worth striving for.

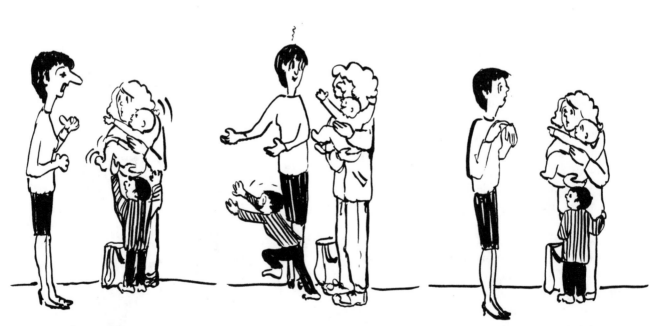

I've decided I'm fed up with you sponging on me......

Come in. Come in......

Oh, I'm just going out to visit my mother.....

TABLE 1A: FOUR WAYS OF BEHAVING

Below are four lists of words linked with four different ways of behaving. It can be quite wrong to judge people by their behaviour, of course — remember that a person may be quite assertive while behaving in ways that do not look assertive. Normally, however, the last approach below is the only one that is genuinely assertive. Which of these approaches do you tend to use?

APPROACH	ASSOCIATED WORDS	BODY LANGUAGE	EFFECT
AGGRESSIVE	Offensive, hostile, pushy, disrespectful, explosive, brutal, barbed, putting down, heavy handed, rough angry, abusive bossy, blaming.	Voice raised, pointing finger, glaring eyes, fist clenched	Hurts people. Antagonises. Makes enemies. Others learn to be aggressive.
PASSIVE	Spiritless, oppressed, grin-and-bear-it, submissive, held back, miserable, weak-kneed, silent, apologetic, over-anxious 'powerless', timid.	Apologetic tone, hands fidget, avoids eye contact, hunched shoulders,	Becomes a doormat. Is not respected. Self-respect lessens. Child becomes irresponsible.
DISHONEST	Sarcastic, indirect two-faced, resentful, manipulating, ratty, repressed anger taken out on others, petty, niggling, uses guilt, cynical, false.	Mixture of aggressive and passive body language.	Hurts others indirectly. Manipulates with guilt. Creates ill-feeling. People don't know where they stand.
ASSERTIVE	Positive, direct, free, steady, honest, relaxed, respectful, quiet, courageous, open, angry in healthy ways, personal, humorous, peaceful, patient, calm, just, encouraging, friendly.	Relaxed body posture, calm voice, steady eye contact.	Others feel respected. Self-esteem and self-confidence grow. Teaches others to respect.

TABLE 1B: TIPS ON BEHAVING ASSERTIVELY

Here are some tips on behaving assertively *that have helped many people — though some of the examples may not be appropriate for your situation. Beware of labelling people — bear in mind that there is no such thing as an 'assertive person' — or an aggressive or passive person. We are usually assertive in some respects and lacking in assertiveness in other respects.*

1. MAKE A HABIT OF SPEAKING *PERSONALLY*

'I like that kind of music'. 'As an unemployed person/woman/Christian I have a problem with that'. 'I think this meeting shouldn't last more than an hour'. 'I love you'. 'I don't think that video is suitable'.

2. BE DIRECT IN LETTING PEOPLE KNOW WHAT YOU WANT

'I need a break'. 'I'd like to be on my own for an hour or so'. 'I don't want you to come this weekend — that doesn't suit me'. 'I'd like a cup of tea'. 'No, I'd prefer not to make love tonight'. 'I'd like to travel with John'.

3. SAY WHAT YOU'RE *FEELING* — NOT JUST WHAT YOU'RE *THINKING.*

'I've had a late night, so I'm tired and in bad form'. 'This is going over my head — I'm feeling confused and lost — please explain it again'. 'When you speak to me like that, I feel a bit frightened — like a little boy in front of a cross teacher'. 'That word offends me as a woman'. 'That was a difficult situation and I'm really impressed with the way you handled it'.

4. SPEAK *TO* A PERSON — RATHER THAN *ABOUT* A PERSON

'I had a sense of being ignored by you and I felt quite taken aback'. 'That remark offends me. I wonder what you mean by it'. 'This is the third time in a week that you've come home late, and I'm angry'.

5. ASK QUESTIONS, LISTEN, AND BE PREPARED TO MAKE SOME CHANGES — INSTEAD OF ARGUING OR GOING ON THE DEFENSIVE.

'I wonder why you said that?'. 'Can you say a bit more?'. 'That's how I see it, but I know you see it differently — how do *you* feel about it?'. 'Tell me what you think would make you happier'. 'No, I'm not prepared to let you go to the hotel disco, but you can go to the Club Disco on Friday'.

COMMENTS FROM PARENTS

He came in and sat down amid the chaos in the kitchen. Never offered to tidy or help with the dinner. I used to fume inside and go into a silent bad mood. But this time I just said 'Larry, I can't cope. You can tidy or you can help with the meal - which would you rather do?' And it worked. Just asking worked.

I feel freer and more confident when I'm assertive. It definitely reduces stress. And I've learnt to fight more realistic battles instead of going around like a bull in a china-shop trying to change everything that's wrong.

When you've a disabled child like mine you need help or you'd go mad. But I couldn't ask for help. Partly because I thought it was my duty to look after her, and partly because I didn't want to be a burden on anyone. It was such a self-defeating attitude.

Until five in the morning the music was blaring from the flat upstairs. I was terribly upset. A number of times I almost went up to complain, but I was frightened of unpleasantness. The next day I had my chance. They said they hoped the music hadn't bothered me and you know what I said? I said 'No, not at all. I hardly heard it!' I need this course!

There was very bad feeling at work. The dishwasher was broken and we were expected to wash all the dishes from the previous shift. The staff were shouting at the supervisor. But it was getting us nowhere. I went over to her and asked to talk to her on her own. Then I told her I respected her personally but we felt we hadn't been treated with respect. She gave in then, and we agreed to do different work.

Our marriage split up because we were going through a rough patch and I thought 'I have to be assertive here and look after myself and get out.' I know some marriages have to split up, but I don't think ours had to. There's always going to be pain in life, and I thought I could escape it, but I caused more pain than ever - to myself as well as to others.

I asked my teenage daughter to get me some carrots at the shop. 'Carrots?' she said, 'I wouldn't be seen dead walking down the street holding carrots!' 'I'm preparing the dinner,' I said, 'I need carrots, and I'd love you to get them. There's no one else who can get them.' 'Then we'll do without,' she said. I know assertive people don't always get what they want, but I felt really disheartened. And yet, I think I did get my way on another level. We had to do without carrots for dinner, but Karen knew she had been selfish - much more than if I had nagged and scolded.

It annoys me a lot to see someone throwing litter out of a car, but I never did anything about it until last week. When I saw a take-away container being dumped into the street, I went over and asked the driver a question: 'Did I see someone just throw that out of the car?' Silence, and a sheepish look. 'I find that disgusting,' I said, and walked away. I didn't try to humiliate the driver, or insist on the litter being picked up, but I do think he'll think twice before he throws litter out of a car again.

CASE STUDIES

Here are some examples of how people might deal with situations in each of the four ways:

A. Your friend comes to your house two or three times a week with two children and stays for hours. You understand that this friend is lonely, but you are not getting your own work done - and the house is generally left in a mess.

Aggressive 'I've decided I'm fed up with you sponging on me - has it never occurred to you that I have *my* work to do?

Passive 'Come in. Come in. And how are the two little darlings this morning?'

Dishonest 'Oh, I'm just going out to visit my mother. Why don't you come back another time?'

Assertive 'Sharon, I'm not free at the moment. I have a lot of work to catch up on this morning. But I do need to talk to you about your visits. I wonder when we could have a chat - perhaps when the children are in bed, so that we can talk without interruption?'

B. Your employer expects you to do extra work, but is not paying you anything extra.

Aggressive Go on the attack, demanding higher wages.

Passive Work hard and say nothing - for 'peace'.

Dishonest Complain to everyone else except the boss.

Assertive Arrange a time to sit down and talk directly to the boss about what you need and want, and negotiate with her/him.

Form into groups of three and talk about what you think someone might say or do in the following situations if they were 1) aggressive 2) passive 3) dishonest 4) assertive.

C. Your daughter often interrupts you and demands your attention when your friend comes in for a chat.

D. The music from your neighbour's stereo is so loud that you can hear it in the garden and all over the house.

E. Your mother expects you for Christmas dinner - as usual. You want to spend Christmas Day at home.

F. Your doctor has just told you that you have arthritis, but he's busy and you find it hard to ask for more information.

G. You want to ask the children to take a fair share of the responsibility for the household chores.

H. Your mother-in-law is smothering you with advice about how to look after your new baby.

Another example from your own experience...

SKILL PRACTICE

Form pairs and take turns in dealing assertively with a few of the situations from the CASE STUDIES. You might use some of the approaches suggested in the TIPS above. For each situation, first talk about what approach you'll take; then try it out; next, say how you felt about that; finally get feedback from your partner on how you came across.

PLANNING FOR
NEXT WEEK

1. Assertiveness is in the mind. And the mind may have to be reprogrammed to deny the many negative messages it has come to believe and have them replaced with positive messages. Pick one of the Rights from the front of the book that you find difficult to accept and repeat it often to yourself during the coming week: 'I have the right to...' It also helps to put aside a few minutes each evening to become aware of how you have been assertive and failed to be assertive during that day, and to think ahead to the following day, seeing yourself acting assertively in one situation you will meet.

2. Tick any of the following people with whom you would *like* to be more assertive:

A demanding child; your mother/father; your partner; a bossy sister or brother; insensitive or interfering in-laws; people who come to your door fundraising; salespeople; a friend; a neighbour; people in an organisation or church you belong to; your doctor; your employer; someone you work with.

Pick one or two situations where you will be more assertive in the coming week (not big ones - it is important to go for small manageable ones for a start. That will give you the confidence to tackle bigger issues later!) Then pair with someone else and plan as specifically as possible what approach you will take, where, when, etc:

And reward yourself with some little treat every time you are assertive this week! What is something you enjoy? Reading a newspaper or magazine? Listening to a tape? Going for a walk?..

1. Who do I need to be more assertive with? In what situation? What will I do?

_____

2. When will I make time each evening to become aware and to think ahead to the following day?

_____

CHAPTER TWO: SAYING 'NO'

An unwanted guest

It was one of those days. So many things to do and no time to do them. Now the telephone was ringing, just as Martina was about to go out to the shop. She picked it up.

'Hello?.. Martina speaking.'

'Martina! How are you? Gee, it's just great to hear that accent. This is Mike Howard. You don't know me, but I have a very dear friend in Melbourne, John Reynolds. I believe he's a second cousin of yours and he insisted I look you up as soon as I arrived.'

'John Reynolds? I.. Er.. Yes.. I think my mother used to speak of some Reynolds cousins in Melbourne. And you said you were..?'

'Howard. Mike Howard. John is a good friend of mine.'

'So where are you ringing from now?'

'I'm in Stonebridge, Martina. And I thought I'd like to come and visit with your family today. And maybe I could stay with you for a few days.'

'Stay with us.. Er.. Yes, well.. we'd love to have you, but we don't have very much room at the moment. I mean..'

'Oh, don't worry about that. Gee, I can bed down on the floor.'

'Oh, no, that won't be necessary - I'm sure we can sort it out. So what time will you be here?'

Not at all. No problem. We'll be delighted...

'Lemme see. Is there any way you could collect me from Stonebridge. I understand I'm just about twenty-five miles from you.'

'Er.. Collect you. Well, yes, I'm sure one of us could pick you up. Where exactly are you in Stonebridge?'

'Right now I'm in the lobby of the Stonebridge Hotel. Can you pick me up here, say at three o'clock?'

'Right. That will be fine. So...it will be very nice to meet you, Mr Howard.'

'Great. Gee, I hope this isn't putting you out.'

'Not at all. No problem. We'll be delighted to have you.'

A firm, polite 'no'

Martina can't say 'no', even to complete strangers. Hospitality and kindness are marvellous virtues, but taking the line of least resistance with someone who acts in a pushy way has little to do with virtue and may have more to do with weakness. And it is quite common.

So what can you do? How do you begin to cope with the enormous number of requests or demands made on your time, attention and pocket today - Can I have more....? Can I get a computer for my birthday? Can I sit up late to watch TV? Will you do more overtime? Can you have that ready for this evening? Will you join...? Will you fix...? How do you deal respectfully with these, yet say 'no' firmly and politely when you need to - especially to your children, partner or family?

There are a number of different approaches illustrated in Table Two at the end of this chapter. To sum them up briefly, it is suggested that you ask questions and find out more about what is being asked - and that you remember you always have the right to ask for time to think. **If you then decide that you need to say 'no', give your reasons, and say 'no' firmly but without aggression - and do *use* the word 'no'.** Watch your tone of voice and body language. Sometimes a 'no' is not firm because you are apologising or explaining too much, or because you're giving a double message, smiling and trying to look sweet in the hope that you'll be liked in spite of your 'no'!

If your 'no' is *not* being respected, however - that is, if the other person is being rude or disrespectful - you may need to consider using the 'broken record' method. This means repeating the same sentence again and again, without any further explanations or excuses. 'No, you can't have another biscuit... Yes, I'm sure I do sound mean, but you can't have another biscuit... I don't think you've heard me - you can't have another biscuit...' If you make excuses or give reasons to someone who is badgering you or treating you disrespectfully, they will often use them against you to hook you into further arguments or discussion, and may then push you into doing what they want. Let the person know that you hear what they are saying, of course - it is not necessary to be rude or impolite. Let's look at some examples:

A slumber party? What's that?

'You don't trust me!'

Julie: 'Can I go to a slumber party?'
Eleven year old Julie eyed her father uncertainly.

Dad: 'A slumber party? What's that?'
Julie raised her eyes in despair at how ill-informed her father was about things that really mattered.

Julie: 'It's just a birthday party where we bring sleeping bags and stay over for the night. Everybody does it now.'

Dad: 'Whose party is it?'
Julie: Angela Brown's.'
Dad: 'Mm. Who else will be there?'
Julie: 'Three or four others. They're all from my class. Elaine will be there too. Can I go?'
Dad: 'What does Mum say?'
Julie: 'She says to ask you.'
Dad: 'Well, I'm open to it. I'll just have to have a word with Helena's mum.'
Julie: 'Aw, Dad, do you have to make such a big fuss about it!'
Dad: 'No big fuss, Julie. It's just to protect you.'
Julie: 'You don't trust me! You think I'm making up a story about the party, and you want to check up on me!'
Dad: (calmly) 'Oh, it's not a question of trust. I have responsibilities as a parent, and I wouldn't be happy about you going to stay even in my *sister's* house unless I made some contact with her.'
Julie: 'Oh, all right!'

This is a shortened version of how Julie's father dealt with the request. He really wasn't sure at first, so you notice he asked questions and talked about what was involved. This also gave him the chance to talk at a personal level about his concerns and values ('I wouldn't be happy about..' is a more helpful approach than a blank 'No, you can't!') Note that he remained calm throughout - he didn't fall into the common patterns of becoming defensive or aggressive. And it was no harm for Julie to have to give in a little bit in order to get her way - a little negotiation is often called for.

But let's take it a stage further and look at an example of a parent saying *'no'* to a request.

Can we go camping?

'Mum, I've a big favour to ask.'
The tone of voice was just right, particularly coming from fourteen year old Fiona, who so often sounded removed and indifferent. Her approach now was disarming.

'Robert and Tim have invited Jane and me to go camping with them for a weekend in May. Please.. can we?'

'Two boys and two girls sleeping together in a tent?,' said Fiona's mum, with an instinctive reaction. 'No, I don't think so.'

'Aw, Mum! Why not?'
'Because you're too young.'
'No, we're not. Please.'
Mum spoke gently but firmly 'No, I'm not prepared to let you go.'

'But that's totally unreasonable. What could happen to us? It's not as if we're going with strangers!'

'I know. As far as I know they're good lads. And it's nice of them to offer, but I think you're just too young to be spending the night in a tent with two boys, and I'm not prepared to let you go.'

(Angrily) 'But what's wrong with camping with two boys! Do you think we're going to get pregnant or something!'

'I have a lot of trust in you, Fiona, but I don't think you're old enough for this and I'm not

17

prepared to let you go!'

'Old enough! Don't come on the heavy! You're just old-fashioned!'

'I'm sure I *do* sound old-fashioned to you, but I'm not prepared to let you go.'

'You're worse than old-fashioned. You're absolutely ridiculous! This is so stupid!'

'I can understand you being angry, but no, I'm not prepared to let you go.'

When you're being badgered

You may not agree with the mother's decision - we are all different, and there is not just one way to deal with a request like this - but it is an example of a firm 'no', with some use of the 'broken record' technique when that became necessary towards the end. All of us have to say 'no' from time to time, and Fiona's mother did so gently but firmly. Fiona then changed from being quite pleasant to being disrespectful, but her mother stayed fairly calm and reasonable. She fixed on one phrase with a clear message 'I'm not prepared to let you go.' However, instead of just repeating this phrase over and over, she also continued to show that she was listening and was hearing what her daughter was saying. **That respectful approach is part and parcel of the 'broken record' method - using this method should never be an excuse for being aggressive or disrespectful.**

Let's look now at another example of 'broken record', for it is a very powerful method in the

Aw Mum! Why not?

hands of anyone who is being badgered or disrespected (and parents today experience a great deal of badgering!) What makes it powerful is that people on the receiving end of it quickly get the message that they are up against a stone wall and that you are not going to change your mind. It is also fairly easy to use, because you repeat the same phrase no matter what arguments or abuse the other person uses. If you do hear something new, however, it is important to stop repeating your 'no', to ask a question, and to show that you really are open to listening. **'Broken record' should only be used in situations where you are being abused and your rights are not being respected.**

Dealing with officialdom

Davina Wesley was beginning to feel hopeless. It was a feeling she often had when dealing with officialdom - the dole office, a large store, the health centre. She had just returned an anorak bought the previous day. She had the receipt, and the shop was happy to take back the anorak, but she could not get her money back. They would give her a credit note - nothing else. That did not suit her, as it was not a shop where she wanted to buy something else.

Her rights were not being respected, she felt, so she decided to refuse to take the credit note and insist on her money. She chose her 'broken record' phrase, looked directly at the assistant, and said

'No, I will only accept cash.'

'I'm sorry, madam, it is our policy only to give credit notes,' the assistant said.

Davina was about to say that she wasn't going to take a credit note when she remembered that repeating the *same* phrase was crucial.

'I understand what you're saying about your policy, but I will only accept cash.'

'But I can't give you cash,' the assistant protested, 'I don't have authorisation.'

Davina kept eye-contact, though she didn't feel as calm as she looked. She was tempted to talk about her rights, but she stuck to the one phrase:

'Perhaps you don't, but I will only accept cash.'

'Look,' said the assistant, 'If I could give you the money, I would. But I tell you I can't.'

'I appreciate that your hands are tied,' Davina replied, respectfully, 'But I will only accept cash.'

The assistant, conscious of a growing queue at the cash desk, felt anxious.

'I'm afraid,' she said, 'I'll have to get the manager to talk to you.'

While the assistant was gone for the manager,

I'm not going to leave until you give me my money back

Davina began to have cold feet. 'Am I just being a crank?' she wondered. There were now four customers waiting in the queue behind her, and she was afraid of being a nuisance to them. But she knew these were common thoughts for people who are fearful of being assertive. And she also knew that waiting customers were to her advantage.

The manager arrived, cold-faced, annoyance in his eyes. There was a hint of bullying in his tone of voice.

'I'm sorry, madam, we never give cash back. If you wish, you can choose something else, or take a credit note.

He's trying to browbeat me, Davina thought, and she grew more determined.

'I hear what you're saying, but I will only accept cash.' she said.

'Really, madam, it's unfair to all these customers to keep them waiting..'

Davina spoke steadily, actually feeling confident now, and looking directly at the manager. If she had to, she even felt prepared to sit on the floor at the cashdesk.

'I realise that you have a problem with customers waiting, but I will only accept cash.'

'Give her the money,' the manager said with disgust, and strode away.

Respect comes from within

Davina was tempted to go after him and insist on being treated with respect, but then she remembered that she had treated *herself* with respect, had stood up for her rights and refused to take 'no' for an answer. **Her self-worth did not depend on the manager. Respect comes from within.**

To sum up. For a variety of reasons, some people, faced with a request or demand, have difficulty in saying 'no'. Yet there are some quite simple ways of dealing with these situations. First, you ask questions and listen. Second, you always have the right to ask for time to think. Then you say a clear 'yes' or 'no', stating your reasons - and negotiating if necessary. If you are not being respected, there is no need to be aggressive or apologetic - just state your position and calmly repeat it again and again. With a little practice, you can be firm but gentle, more assertive and more confident in dealing with the many requests and demands you meet today.

You always have the right to ask for time to think.

TABLE TWO: DEALING WITH REQUESTS OR DEMANDS

Here are three stages for dealing with people who come at you with requests or demands. It is important to be flexible, of course. For example, there is obviously no need to work down through these stages in dealing with most normal requests! Or it may be quite appropriate to being dealing with a demand at stage three.

'CAN I GO TO THE DISCO, DAD?'

STAGE ONE: YOU'RE NOT SURE . (OPEN ENDED)

FIND OUT MORE — ASK QUESTIONS

'Until what time? Who'll be there? Who's supervising?'

SAY YOU NEED TIME

'I'll need some time to think and talk to your Mum about it'.

THEN NEGOTIATE CONDITIONS

'Coming home time? Alcohol? Driver? Yes. I'm prepared to let you go . . . . . provided'.

STAGE TWO: IF THE ANSWER IS "NO" . . (REASONABLE 'NO')

SAY 'NO' POLITELY AND FIRMLY (WATCH YOUR BODY LANGUAGE)

'No'. I don't want you to go because . . . . . .

SAY WHY CLEARLY — GIVE YOUR REAL REASONS, NOT 'EXCUSES'

'I'm not happy about the drinking and general behaviour at that disco. It's a bad atmosphere'.

DON'T REJECT THE PERSON — AND IF POSSIBLE OFFER ALTERNATIVES

'I know it's hard if you were counting on going, but you may go to the Club Disco if you wish'

STAGE THREE: IF YOUR 'NO' IS NOT RESPECTED . (BROKEN RECORD 'NO')

KEEP REPEATING YOUR 'NO'

'Yes, I know it's more difficult when you've made plans with your friends, but I don't want you to go'.

KEEP LISTENING AND REMAIN POLITE (WITH BODY LANGUAGE TO MATCH)

'Mm, I can see that creates problems — but I don't want you to go'. (Steady eye contact, good posture, calm voice, stay friendly)

GIVE NO FURTHER EXPLANATIONS — JUST REPEAT SAME PHRASE.

'Yes, I hear what you're saying, but I don't want you to go'.

COMMENTS FROM PARENTS

Our nineteen year old daughter has been unemployed for a few months and has constantly been asking us for money. Yet for some reason she wouldn't sign on for the dole money she was entitled to. After the last session, we decided to say a polite 'no' to her requests for money and cigarettes - and it worked; she has just signed on the dole!

One of the things that has pleased me is that I have (most of the time) been able to say a *friendly* 'no'. I had thought that you had to be cross and a bit aggressive in order to say 'no' firmly.

During the week, I noticed how apologetic one of my workmates was whenever he said 'no'. It was interesting - he usually blamed somebody else or went into long explanations. You could see he wasn't comfortable. I thought to myself 'He *really* needs a course!'

It feels hard and cruel to say 'no' to the children. On one level I know it's right, but I can't help feeling guilty.

It's certainly making me more aware of body language and how much I give away with the expression on my face and my tone of voice. The children pick that up automatically. I can't remember what I said to my three year old last week, but he shocked me by asking 'Why did you say it with a cross face?'

What I like about the course is that it's positive. It's about being polite and respectful to others as well as to myself.

When I have to say 'no', I find that I kind of brace myself in advance for a reaction, so my 'no' comes out tough and aggressive - which actually *creates* a lot of anger in my children.

I'm a very passive person. I certainly would never have seen myself as aggressive. I mean, I don't use threats with the children, I don't smack them, or shout at them. So it has been a revelation to discover that my body language and tone of voice is full of aggression. Now I know why I'm not more successful as a parent. Body language seems to be the key.

This seems to be a 'biggie' for parents. I find children make far more demands today than when I was a child - and it's really not good to give them everything they ask for. Life's not like that. We *have* to learn to say 'no'.

While I was sitting in the pub, a few men came around collecting money in pint glasses for 'deprived children'. I knew it wasn't official, but I gave them a pound because I was afraid of them. I think I'll be stronger the next time.

When they asked me to go with them, I said I needed to think about it. I've always said 'yes' to them before because it's so hard for me to say 'no', so at least that was an improvement.

GETTING IN TOUCH: SESSION TWO:
WHY IT'S DIFFICULT TO SAY 'NO'

Tick any of these reasons why you find it difficult to say 'no' - even sometimes. Then underline the reason that seems to most prevent you from being assertive in saying 'no'.

✓ **I'm afraid of hurting the other person.**

I'm afraid of the other person's anger.

I'm afraid of not being liked.

Somehow I've picked up that a good mother/ father doesn't say 'no'.

I feel sorry for the person who comes to my door.

Doctors (and professional people) know best anyway.

✓ **I find it hard to make decisions - I'm often torn and unsure.**

✓ **It makes me feel guilty and uncomfortable to say 'no'.**

✓ **I upset plans and I'm a nuisance if I say 'no'.**

It feels rude and selfish to say 'no', at least without making excuses.

Good people (or Christian people) shouldn't say 'no'.

I lose my nerve when i meet people in authority, so I say 'yes'.

✓ **It's easier to give in and do what someone else expects.**

Another reason........

Take a few minutes to share your answers with the person beside you (opposite side to the last time). Can you think of a time when you wanted to say 'no' but didn't:

CASE STUDIES

Mark each of the following situations with a 1, 2, or 3, according to which of the three approaches in Table Two you would use. Then form into groups of three and take a few minutes to have a little chat about what you marked. Please respect the point of view of anyone who differs from you.

1. You have told you daughter she must be in bed for ten. She is now angry and disrespectful, and full of arguments why you should change your mind.

2. You're on holidays, walking down the street, when two young women approach you, smiling and very chatty, but inviting you very insistently to come to a presentation on buying time-share holiday homes.

3. Your husband/ wife wants to buy something which you see as a luxury, and your finances are already overstretched.

4. A man whom you don't know has offered you a lift home in his car.

5. You have been asked to join a committee to organise the Christmas jumble sale, and they won't take 'no' for an answer.

6. Your partner has a drink problem and is using lots of arguments to get you to give him/ her more money.

7. Earlier this evening, your daughter spent two hours watching TV, and now says 'I have to stay up late to finish my homework'.

8. Someone at your door is collecting for a Charity you don't want to support.

9. Your mother-in law wants to come and stay at a time that doesn't really suit you.

10. You have told your son (aged 3) that he may not have a biscuit until he has eaten his dinner, but he keeps asking for it in the hope of wearing you down.

SKILL PRACTICE

For the skill practice, you're asked to stay in your group of three, and to practise the 'broken record' method. Choose any one of the 'Case Study' situations where the person is being badgered - or, better still, a suitable example from your own life. One of you will be acting assertively; a second will be the one making the request; and the third will be the observer. Each time, you can stop after a minute and comment on how you think you got on, then allow the observer to comment, possibly mentioning

● **Your posture - comfortable, hunched, apologetic?..**

● **Your eye-contact - direct, open, glaring, steady?..**

● **Expression on your face - cross, relaxed?..**

● **Your tone of voice - harsh, gentle, raised, calm, angry?..**

● **Overall - polite and respectful but firm?..**

You're asked to do this exercise three times, with three different situations, but changing roles each time - each person will have a chance to act assertively, to be the one making the request, and to be the observer.

PLANNING FOR NEXT WEEK

What are one or two fairly typical situations where you will need to deal with requests/ demands? How will you deal with one of them?

It is also suggested that you take a little time each evening to relax your body and mind and become *aware* of how assertive you have been, and then foresee how you will act in one situation you will be meeting the following day. Notice how you normally act, and then see yourself acting assertively - with love and self-

control. Note little details like your surroundings and what you'll be wearing - the more vividly you see it all, the more likely you are to be assertive. You may have to do this for a number of days before you see a difference in how you behave, but this daily exercise can have a powerful effect in helping you make these skills your own in a natural way. Such awareness can be the key to effective change.

1. When will I take time each day to become aware and to foresee my behaviour?

_____

2. When am I likely to meet with a request/ demand soon? How will I deal with it?... Feel free to talk this out with the person beside you.

_____

CHAPTER THREE: DEALING WITH ABUSE AND CRITICISM

'He sounded so clever that everyone else laughed, but I felt it like a barb, for it made me look small and stupid. I wanted to stand up for myself, but then it might have looked as if I was making a mountain out of a molehill. Besides, the conversation had passed on to something else before I had time to think. Anyway... I suppose you can't afford to be too sensitive these days. I mean, my children say hurtful things like that to me all the time. You learn to live with things...'

Bowing to criticism - or fighting back?

Many of you can possibly identify with much of what this parent is saying. Criticism and abuse can take many different shapes. They are seldom raw and crude - 'You're a ******* pig!' There may be no words spoken at all. It may be a dirty look - or just the fact that you're ignored or interrupted or overlooked. Or the words used may be perfectly harmless, but with just a hint of sarcasm or aggression - or said in a patronising, superior tone of voice - and you know you're being put down. Yet it happens so quickly, or it seems too small to make a fuss about, so you say nothing. You *allow* yourself to be put down; you remain passive and oppressed in the face of abuse.

Within a family, however, people are not usually so timid. Far from accepting criticism or abuse passively, they will often feel free to lash back and give as good as they get, caring little about the consequences. It's a good thing to fight, of course - it's certainly better than smiling and bottling up your feelings - but naked aggression will hardly get you very far. **Meeting abuse with abuse is destructive.** Neither of the approaches above is an assertive - or helpful - way to deal with abuse.

Asking questions

How, then, can you deal effectively with criticism and abuse so as not to lose your dignity and self-respect - and at the same time show respect to the other person? Let's look at an example.

Fifteen year old Philip Harris was arguing with his mother, and things were not going his way, so he became quite rude and disrespectful.

'You're a stupid bitch!' he shouted.

Adolescents need to rebel. But Philip's statement is not just rebellion. It is abuse. And **abuse - physical or emotional - is never acceptable. It is always wrong.** Mrs Harris has a number of assertive options. She can choose to

Why did you call me that?

go quiet and ignore her son, perhaps leaving the room. Or she can impose some sanctions on the spot, like stopping pocket-money, until he apologises. Each family's situation is different, and there is no simple approach that applies across the board. But **one effective way of dealing with abuse is to ask a direct question.** 'Why did you say that?' 'What do you mean by...?' This is what Mrs Harris chose to do.

'What did you say?' she asked.

'You heard me the first time.'

'I'm just checking that I heard right. What did you call me?'

Philip didn't want to repeat what he had said, for he was now beginning to feel a bit foolish, but he remained stubborn.

'You heard' he repeated.

'Why did you call me that?' his mother asked.

'Because you *are* stupid.' he said lamely.

Mrs Harris remained calm, but her questions were relentless.

'I'd like to know why you say I'm stupid?' she asked.

The questions were beginning to get to Philip.

'Oh, forget about it!' he muttered.

'Does that mean you're taking back your insult?' his mother asked. 'Because I *can't* forget about it. I feel insulted by what you called me.'

'No, I'm not taking it back.' he said, hoping that might be the end of it. But his mother did not go off in a huff; she continued to 'level' with him.

'So where do we go from here then?' she asked.

'Wherever you like. I don't care. I'm going out.'

'I don't like you walking out in the middle of an argument.'

'Hard luck!' he said. And he went out.

The value of questions

Many parents live with this kind of disrespect and abuse. It is not surprising that they often hit back and say equally hurtful and disrespectful things to their children. It becomes a vicious circle then. To break that cycle, all it takes is for one person to refuse to be sucked into the bickering and slanging, to choose instead to be assertive. That is what Mrs Harris had done.

It may appear that she wasn't very successful in asserting herself - in that Philip maintained his hostile front and refused to apologise. But **being assertive does not guarantee that you will win, or that the other person will change. Being assertive is not about winning or getting your own way.** The goal is to keep your dignity, refusing to let yourself be put down by the disrespect you experience. In order to make this point more clearly, we have deliberately chosen an example of assertiveness here where the parent did *not* get her own way.

And yet, Mrs Harris' questions were not just good for herself, helping her to maintain her dignity and self-respect. They were also good for her son. For her questions were forcing Philip to repeat his abusive remark and to hear more clearly what he had just said. He was so anxious to save face, of course, that he would not admit to being embarrassed or sorry, so he was unco-operative in answering his mother's questions, yet she continued to confront him. People will often hedge or stall or give evasive answers when they are confronted with direct questions. They will say something like 'I don't know' or 'That's why'. You may feel frustrated and be tempted to stop at that - just when your abuser* is feeling uncomfortable and trying to escape. It may be important to cut through this hedging with further questions 'What do you mean you don't know?' - or to repeat the question, as Philip's mother did, indicating that she was not satisfied with the answer. The result was that his mother gave Philip a lot to think about and he

You hate me! Everybody hates me!

did feel distinctly uncomfortable at the end of the encounter. This often happens when you confront an abuser with direct questions. You help them to think about what they are saying.

'Levelling' with people

The other assertive thing which Mrs Harris did was to speak personally ('I feel insulted' 'I don't like..') This openness is ofen called 'levelling' because it cuts through any pretences, and calls for a certain basic equality and respect in a relationship. **Talking at the level of feelings can be particularly helpful, for your feelings can face people, including teenagers and young people, into the *effects* of their abuse.** They can feel quite sobered when you say something like 'I feel hurt by what you've just said'. And that can be a gift to them.

There is another great advantage to 'levelling' and being real, even admitting some of the faults you're being accused of. Your openness will usually help your critic to talk, to express some of their own frustration, anger and pain - which is often the real problem behind their criticism. When people blame, criticise or abuse you, it's good to remember that they may be annoyed about something completely different, something that has nothing to do with you. They may be in considerable pain in their own personal lives, and are just taking it out on you because you happen to be closest to them - or because you're the first person they've met. In a case like that, there are two things at stake - one, you need to

* We have decided to use the word 'abuser' for verbal and emotional abuse in order to highlight the pain such abuse causes.

keep your dignity and not let yourself be put down; and, two, there is a person with you who is in pain and needs to be helped to express it. You might begin by suggesting: 'Why don't we sit down and have a chat about it?' 'Levelling', listening, and showing understanding may then be much better than asking questions. We'll look at an example.

'Stop interfering in my life!'

Janine Wall felt devastated. At thirteen, she was becoming a young woman and was bewildered by the changes in her body and in her moods. She was often irritable and impatient now, and she knew she was a pain to her family and friends - but she was an even bigger pain to herself; she just didn't seem to have any control over her sudden mood swings. Now she had exasperated her best friend, Natalie, and Natalie had made it obvious that she didn't want to be her friend any more.

She arrived home from school. Her younger brother, Ronnie, stood in the hallway, playfully blocking her passage. She kicked him. When her father arrived to investigate the shouting, she turned on him.

'Get stuffed!' she screamed, 'You're always interfering in my life. Just hump off and leave me alone.'

'Janine,' he said, 'I won't have you treat us like that. I want you to go to your room and to stay there until you're prepared to treat us with respect.'

...until your firm 'No' gives them an excuse to cry...

'Respect!' she spat, as she turned on her heel, 'You have to *earn* respect. You hate me! Everybody hates me! And I hate the whole lot of you.'

Levelling and listening

It would have been pointless for Mr Walker to ask questions or challenge Janine on the things she had just said - partly because they weren't the real issue, and partly because she was too angry and upset to talk. By setting some limits and giving her a cooling off period, he was taking a more helpful approach. He left her alone for an hour to give her (and himself!) a chance to simmer down. Then he went to her room.

'I need to talk to you, Janine,' he said, 'But I know you're upset right now. When will you be ready to talk?'

It was a good start, no ultimatum, with an openness to negotiate.

'Not much point in talking,' she said, coldly, 'I've nothing to say. But if *you* want to talk you can talk now.'

'Yes, I'd like to chat,' he said, sitting down and looking directly at his daughter. 'I honestly don't know where I stand with you, or what approach to take, Janine. I'm lost. I don't know what's happening between us.'

Janine had expected toughness, at least a lecture. Instead, her father was being honest with her and making himself vulnerable. Inside, she melted a little, but it was too difficult to drop her aggressive front as yet.

'If you'd stop interfering and let me live my life my way!' she said angrily.

'You see me interfering in your life...'

'Yes, you *are* interfering. If I have a fight with Ronnie, that's *my* business and I want you to stay out of it. How would you like it if you had someone nagging at you as soon as you arrived in from work?'

He wanted to say that it *was* his business if she was abusing her younger brother, but this wasn't the time for scoring points. Better to give her his attention and encourage her to say more.

'So that was how you experienced it - me nagging at you...'

There was a pause. then he continued in a reassuring tone:

'Mm... Life's tough enough at the moment without someone else finding fault with you...'

Slowly, gradually, Janine came round, softened by her father's listening, understanding and openness. Within five minutes, she was in tears, spilling out her misery, her father's arm around her. When she dried her eyes, there was some relief, and life no longer seemed so unbearable. Tomorrow she might be angry again, and might say equally nasty things to him, but she had found **something that adolescents so desperately need - a listening ear and some understanding to help her begin to make sense of a bewildering world.**

Watch for the signals

This approach is not just for adolescents. Children (and adults) of all ages need an understanding ear. Even very young children carry around a great deal of pain. It's not necessarily major things like parents separating or the death of someone close; it can be something as simple as an imagined slight or a falling out of friends. Very often, they will express their pain and discouragement by criticising you and finding fault. They need to be helped to find ways of admitting their own pain and expressing it, whether in words or screams or tears.

Toddlers are great at giving you signals when they need to cry out their misery - 'You're holding me too tight' when you're scarcely touching them, or asking for more and more treats until your firm 'no' gives them an excuse to cry. With older children, it's harder, but the signals are there - often in abusive behaviour. It requires patience and practice to give them the hearing they need while keeping your dignity at the same time and refusing to take abuse. Setting limits, but also levelling, listening and showing understanding, may be just the tools for that.

'Your work is not up to standard'

We have looked now at the two chief skills for dealing with criticism - asking questions and 'levelling', but the examples so far have been of criticism that was destructive. In fact, criticism can be quite *constructive*, and is not at all a bad thing. None of us *likes* to be criticised, but it is *essential* for us to get constructive criticism if we are to improve. Again, asking a question instead of reacting with anger is an assertive way to deal with it that also shows an openness to listening and to changing. Let's look at an example.

Mrs McKay is the supervisor in a mail order firm. She has just sent for one of the packers, Michael Kerr.

'I'm afraid, Michael, your work is not up to standard.'

'Why do you say that?' Michael asked, 'Can you be specific?'

'Well, I've had three complaints from customers in the last week alone. When their orders were supplied, all three of them found

That's really unfair to me...

that there was something missing or incorrect.'

'Mm. That's not so good. Give me the details please, and I'll check them out.'

Half an hour later, Michael returned.

'The incorrect order was my mistake,' he said. 'I'm sorry. I normally double-check each order I make up, and I didn't double-check this one because I was under pressure. The other two orders were not handled by me. You remember I wasn't here on Tuesday.'

'I see. You know *all* orders have to be double-checked, Michael. Pressure of work is no excuse. How are you going to prevent this happening in future?'

'Well, if I'm under pressure, I'll have to shout and make sure I get extra help, or else we'll have to leave some orders till the following day.'

'Okay. That would be better than making them up incorrectly under pressure.'

Michael looked directly at Mrs McKay as he spoke his next sentence.

'There is something I want to say, Mrs McKay. I was quite taken aback this morning when you said my work wasn't up to standard. That was a strong statement, and I think it was unfair and uncalled for. I wonder why you said that?..'

Dealing with constructive criticism

In this situation, we see that Michael began with a certain basic openness. Instead of becoming defensive or going on the attack, as so often happens in such circumstances, Michael asked a question. He asked for specific details.

Secondly, he knew that one of his rights was the right to have some time to think - time to consider the criticism and check it out. Just because you have chosen not to be aggressive does not mean that you *agree* with a criticism, passively accept it, and assume you must be in the wrong!

Thirdly, he came back to the supervisor, accepted responsibility for his mistake, and showed himself open to negotiation and to making some changes. But there was nothing slavish in his approach - indeed, he made a powerful I-statement, making it very clear that he had no intention of allowing himself to be put down or disrespected. He had handled the criticism with an openness and self-respect that was really assertive.

To sum up then. Unless a person is in pain or very upset, it is suggested that you begin dealing with criticism by asking questions. Next, you take some time to think about the criticism and check it out. Then you firmly accept or reject it. And finally, you talk out any changes that you may now need to make.

Constructive criticism, indeed, can be so valuable that it may be a good idea to invite it from time to time. For example, it can be quite an assertive thing occasionally to ask your children for negative feedback. They may tell you how they feel about you listening to the news so much or talking so long to a neighbour when they would love you to play or have more fun with them! It's much easier to listen to criticism when you have taken the initiative.

Other ways of standing up for yourself

As well as asking questions and making personal statements, there are a number of other ways of dealing with abuse or unfair criticisms.

One way is to use 'fogging'. Quite simply, this means dealing with someone who is abusive (for example, a child who does not show you respect and constantly wants to argue and prove you wrong) by saying 'Mm.. Could be.' or 'You've a good point there' or 'Maybe you're right'. The attacker then doesn't know where they stand; you haven't agreed with them, but you haven't disagreed, and it's impossible to fight with an enemy who has just disappeared into the fog. For that is what you do with this method - disappear into a fog without losing face. Hence the expression 'fogging'.

'Broken record' can be another useful way of dealing with people who are criticising you unfairly or putting you down. You deny the criticism clearly and firmly and fix on a phrase that you continue to repeat. 'That is abuse, and I won't let you abuse me.' 'Yes, I accept that you didn't mean it that way, but it's abuse, and I

won't let you abuse me.' 'I know, I appreciate that you're angry, but it's abuse, and I won't let you abuse me...' It is hard to imagine how powerful this can be until you experience it, but people who are on the receiving end of 'broken record', even in a role-play, will often comment on how determined the other person comes across. If genuine grievances or constructive criticism surface, of course, it may be important to stop using 'broken record' and listen. This method should *only* be used when someone is very rude or disrespectful.

And finally, there is the simple technique of *ignoring* a hurtful remark. Your silence may be accompanied by a direct look, serious but not necessarily indignant, or you may prefer to ignore the put-down totally. This can be quite effective. None of us likes to be ignored, so your very silence can leave the abuser smarting and more aware of their own unfairness.

I'm not a machine!

These, then, are some ways of dealing with criticism and abuse that help you keep your dignity and self-respect - levelling, listening, asking questions, asking for time, fogging, 'broken record', and ignoring.

You are not a machine, of course - you may feel angry and frustrated by a put-down. Your self-esteem can take a battering. Being angry and aggressive in return is not the answer - to explode is to lose respect - but you will need to

You are not a machine

do something to restore some calm. Slow breathing, a walk, counting to twenty, listening to music, phoning a friend, or focusing onto something completely different will often help you cope temporarily, but don't ignore your body's real need for a fuller release of the anger at the first opportunity you get - thumping a pillow in the bedroom, having a good cry, scrubbing a floor, screaming (out of hearing of the children), or taking some strenuous exercise. **If you don't release that anger in your own time, it is liable to come out in other ways - in ill-health, depression, or an uncontrolled explosion that can do damage to those you love.**

And when you are ready to talk, you may need to be particularly careful about your tone of voice and body language in order to ensure that your response comes across as genuinely assertive.

thumping a pillow in the bedroom

GETTING IN TOUCH SESSION THREE

Here are some ways in which people can feel put down.

A. Sarcasm 'Oh, you're really thoughtful, I must say.'

B. Being ignored or interrupted.

C. Being patronised. 'Yes, dear.' or 'Here come the girls!'

D. Remarks that label women - 'Must be a woman driver!'

E. Remarks/ jokes that similarly label men, old people, gays.. people of a particular nationality, people who are disabled.

F. People making unfair assumptions (that Mum does the ironing).

G. Hurtful words to describe you - stupid, fool, idiot, nuisance.

H. Being treated as a sex object rather than as a person.

J. Words that are charged - 'Don't be *morbid/ hysterical.*' 'Don't go *raving* on and on - I heard you the first time.'

K. Someone using an angry aggressive tone of voice.

L. Jokes with a barb that hurt you - even if others don't notice!

M. Being sneered at, eg. 'You're always right!/ You know it all!'

Who criticises you or puts you down? (Many of us experience most criticism from members of our own families). Can you remember a specific instance when you experienced that person putting you down, being sarcastic, dismissive, patronising, giving you the silent treatment, interrupting you or being aggressive with you? What did you feel and do?

After a minute or so to reflect, form pairs - opposite side to first exercise - and take a few minutes to share your answers.

TABLE THREE: DEALING WITH ABUSE AND CRITICISM

Below are some ways of dealing with abuse and criticism, but remember that someone who criticises you may be acting out of very strong feelings, including great personal pain. In that case, it may be better to postpone dealing with the situation until later, and then to listen, show understanding, and encourage them to talk.

Child: That's really unfair to me!

STAGE ONE: IF CRITICISM *MAY* BE TRUE . . .

FIND OUT MORE — ASK QUESTIONS
'Why do you say that? — What's unfair about it?'

SAY YOU NEED TIME
'I want to think over what you've said . . . .'

RECOGNISE WHAT'S TRUE IN IT
'I was unaware of what I was doing, and I'm sorry.'

TALK OUT CHANGES
'What will be fairer to both of us? . . . . How can we respect each other more? . . . .'

STAGE TWO: IF CRITICISM IS *NOT* TRUE

LOOK DIRECTLY AT CRITIC AND DENY IT CLEARLY
'I don't accept that it's unfair — we had agreed on what would happen'.

STAGE THREE: IF YOU ARE NOT BEING RESPECTED

When you are being abused or disrespected, avoid arguing or going on the defensive. Feel free to use **any** of the following approaches, or a mixture of them, depending on which you judge to be best in the circumstances. At times, it may be better simply to ignore the remark - or to diffuse the situation by being light and humorous and helping the other person to laugh with you.

KEEP REPEATING	SPEAK PERSONALLY	ASK QUESTIONS	USE 'FOGGING'
I don't accept that . . . I hear what you're saying but I don't accept it.	I feel hurt by that remark. I don't like being labelled.	Why do you say that? . . . Is it fair? . . . What do you hear me saying?	Mm . . . Perhaps You could be right . . .

COMMENTS FROM PARENTS

My oldest boy was complaining about everything. Instead of being aggressive back to him, I asked him 'Why did you say that, Andrew?' He was so confused by my directness that he mumbled an answer, and when I questioned him further, he actually said he was sorry!

At ten past ten I went into her room and asked calmly 'Why did you not put out your lights at ten?' She had no answer. If I had nagged at her, (as I usually do), she would have gone on the attack.

Out of the blue, I invited him to tell me what he wasn't happy with at home. I'm not sure I would recommend that to everyone, because it was hard to listen to. But it was good to hear the criticisms, and he was surprised that I was open to listening to them. I'd like to do that again - occasionally!

I went over the top completely with my daughter last week. She said something sarcastic and I saw red. I was so angry with her that I gave her an ultimatum and left the room. Then I realised how silly it was - I had got myself into a corner instead of staying friendly, which was my only hope. I mean, If you're annoyed about the way you're being treated at work you go to the boss with the goal of getting fairer treatment - you don't go to him to hand out an ultimatum and lose your job. I think it's the same thing. I don't want to lose my daughter. I'm glad I was able to find a way of backing down.

An aggressive person is someone full of feelings and desperate for someone to listen to them. So I think you have to be prepared for the consequences if you ask a question - you have to be prepared to listen.

To me, not treating the furniture with care is a kind of abuse, so I asked 'Why did you kick the door?'. He said, 'I just did it.' So I asked another question 'What have I told you you need to do whenever you have abused people or the furniture?' Again, he tried to escape with a foggy answer 'I don't know.' 'Would you prefer to go to your room and think about it?' I asked. 'No. I remember - I need to say sorry.' he said. Asking a few questions and giving him a choice when he won't co-operate is helping me to be assertive - instead of giving up in despair.

My husband was going out to the club for a drink for 'half an hour', and he asked me to drive. I was happy enough for a while, but every time I suggested going home, he put me off. We eventually got home at three in the morning. I wasn't being respected, and I was too 'nice' about it. I should have driven home and left him there if he didn't want to come.

I don't think you say anywhere that a good way to deal with a cross child - or any difficult person - is to keep your sense of humour. Many a time we could have had a terrible row - completely unnecessarily - if I hadn't joked a bit and stayed light.

I went in full of aggression, but he treated me with such respect that I didn't say all I had planned to say. Instead he listened to me and seemed to understand how I felt. I was impressed. He was actually giving me a great example of being assertive - just cutting through the aggression and getting us talking directly and openly. I liked being treated like that, and it struck me that my children would like me to treat them like that too when they're mad about something.

CASE STUDIES

Form into groups of three and take about five minutes as a group to decide how you might deal with the following put-downs (check Stage 3 of Table 3 for ideas):

Child: You know everything, don't you!
You don't care about me/ You hate me!
Would you shut up!
You wouldn't understand!
Great! Just great! (Sarcastic, with dirty look)
Neighbour: I wouldn't let *my* children do that.
Have you no control over your children!

Someone at work: What are you supposed to be doing!
I'll do it myself. You're making a mess!
You're not even trying!
Professional: I think I know better, dear.
You should really mind your own business.
That's not the way to go about it.

SKILL PRACTICE

This is an exercise to help you deal with abusive remarks in real life. Remain in your groups of three and practise saying an abusive remark from the Case Studies to each other. Each time, it helps to talk out the approach you'll take first, then deal with it in any of the ways suggested for dealing with abuse; next, say how you felt about that; finally get feedback from the observer on tone of voice, body posture, eyes, etc. Change roles for each situation. Where appropriate, feel free to role play the complete situation instead of just the opening lines.

PLANNING FOR NEXT WEEK

Look back to the 'Getting in touch' section to remind yourself of who it is that abuses you. Over the next week, you might tackle one or two fairly simple situations where you meet with abuse or criticism.

It is also suggested that you take a little time each evening to relax your body and mind and become *aware* of how you have been assertive that day. Ask yourself 'When today did I shrink from being honest? When did I choose to speak up, or to communicate more openly, or to refuse to be treated with disrespect?.. Then, foresee how you will act in one situation you will be meeting the following day. Notice how you normally act, and then see yourself acting assertively - with love and self-control. Note little details like your surroundings and what you'll be wearing - the more vividly you see it all, the more likely you are to be assertive. You may have to do this for a number of days before you see the difference in how you behave.

1. When will I take time each day to become aware and to foresee my behaviour?

2. What situation/ who criticises me?... What I'll do... Feel free to talk this out with the person beside you.

32

CHAPTER FOUR: GIVING CONSTRUCTIVE CRITICISM

The years of repressed anger have taken their toll.

Afraid to correct

Elizabeth Barnes wants peace at any price. When her children are unruly and badly behaved, she will make only a gentle protest that is ignored. When her husband expects her to be there for him but takes her for granted and makes his plans without any regard for her, she doesn't question the way things are - 'Thank God,' she says, 'We've never had a fight.' And when her neighbours 'use' her, she murmurs something to the effect that 'that's what I'm here for'.

Because Elizabeth is so afraid of tension, she finds it very difficult to correct anyone. This can actually encourage those close to her to be irresponsible. They do not have to face the consequences of their inconsiderate or disrespectful behaviour. And they are not the only ones to suffer. For she has done all this at enormous cost to herself. The years of repressed anger have taken their toll. She usually looks a bit worn. Her health, her self-image, her humanity have all suffered.

Destructive criticism

People who tend to act passively can be quite reluctant to correct others. But most parents have no such reluctance. We have been well trained by the society we live in to look for the flaws, to find fault. Sometimes we will remain silent, (or dishonest), with people in the community, but within a family many of us tend to be quick to criticise, pointing out faults, nagging, scolding, reminding, threatening. These are aggressive, destructive habits that often take us over and control us.

It damages us to be so negative and critical in our thinking, and it also damages others. Research shows how fragile and delicate human beings are - how they wither with destructive criticism, how they lose confidence in themselves and develop low self-esteem, how they perform worse and fail to achieve a fraction of their potential. **Our criticism usually does much more damage than the behaviour we want to correct.**

Clothes scattered on the floor

So how can we correct in a way that avoids these extremes and that is constructive and helpful? We'll begin with an illustration. Dad needs to correct his daughter about the state in which she has left the bathroom.

Dad: Mary, I need to talk to you. Are you free at the moment?

Mary: Yes, what is it?

Dad: It's about the bathroom. It's over an hour since you've had your bath, but the water is still in the bath and your clothes are scattered on the floor.

I was quite shocked when I went in and found it like that. I need you to clean up the bathroom as soon as you've had a bath.

I know you *intended* to clean it up, Mary - but (teasing) I think I know where your thoughts are these days!

The right moment

You will notice that Mary's father began by checking out that it was a suitable time to talk. That is a respectful approach, and it also means that the other person is more psychologically prepared for the correction.

Very often, parents just wade in and correct their children as soon as they discover something is wrong - without waiting for a suitable moment. This kind of spur-of-the-moment correction has been compared to waving at flies in irritation. It is a useless exercise. The flies will not go away. The irritation will continue. **It is good to ask yourself why you are correcting - because you are annoyed or because you genuinely want to help?** Choosing the right moment, and checking out that it is a suitable time, will usually contribute to the effectiveness of a orrection.

Being specific

Secondly, Mary's father was specific. Instead of talking in general terms ('You just don't care about the state of the bathroom!' or 'You always leave it in a mess.') he gave a concrete, specific example of the annoying behaviour. Note that it is the *behaviour* and not the *person* that is being criticised. **We are never justified in attacking a person's character. We are never justified in calling names or showing disrespect.**

Being specific is very important. People will be much less inclined to argue with you when you know the details and spell them out. If you are not sure of the details, perhaps it is best to postpone correction until you are sure of your ground. Correction needs to be based on *facts*.

Part of being specific, too, is limiting the correction to just one single behaviour. This should not be an opportunity for griping about old sores or a whole host of other annoyances. It is more effective to deal with one problem or

It's about the bathroom.

issue at a time.

Talking to your mother-in-law about the way she interferes with your disciplining of the children, for example, it would be important not to speak generally, accusing her of 'interfering', but to stick to the facts and speak in specific terms, like:

'Yesterday you told the children not to pay any attention to what I had just said to them about hanging up their coats.'

A bald statement of the facts can be very effective. It is not enough on its own, of course - which brings us to the third guideline for giving a correction.

Speaking personally

The third thing you will notice about the father's correction is that he spoke personally. He told Mary how he *felt* about her behaviour and what his *needs* were in the situation. And that is the third guideline. **People are usually far more receptive to a criticism when you use 'I-statements' (about yourself) rather than accuse them with 'you-statements'** - 'I feel nervous' rather than 'You make me nervous', 'I need a break' rather than 'You don't give me a break!', 'It's important to me...' rather than 'It's important for you...'

One word of caution. In giving 'I-messages' it is important to bear in mind that our children are not responsible for how we feel. Our feelings are our own. Someone else in the same situation might feel quite differently. We have to be careful not to offload guilt onto others about how we feel.

So, returning to the correction being given to the mother-in-law, you might continue:

'I know that you were half-joking when you said it, but I felt a bit shocked and taken aback, even undermined - and I saw confusion in the children's faces. It's important to me that they hang up their coats when they come home from school, so I need you to support me - or at least to say nothing if you disagree with the rules I make.'

Speaking personally lets the other person know what you need and expect, and it also faces them into the effects of their behaviour on you. It may take courage, for they may not like what they hear, but it can do them great good.

Ending with a compliment

Mary's father ended his correction by saying a few words of encouragement to her, even being gently humorous and light. And that is the fourth and final guideline for giving constructive criticism. **It is recommended that you end a**

correction with a word of confidence or encouragement, specifically mentioning something positive that you have noticed about the person, and/or expressing your positive feelings. We have just seen that the goal is to criticise the behaviour and not the person. After all, we're dealing with *people* — who may be vulnerable and sensitive. The whole purpose of a correction is to build them up, improve them and encourage them.

In the past, it was often recommended that we should say nice things to people before making a criticism - 'buttering them up' for the blow. That may be helpful, but it is being suggested today that it is even *more* helpful and effective to *follow* a correction with a brief, sincere, specific compliment. In this way, the last thing which the person being corrected hears is positive. That can prevent a defensive reaction, and it allows your goodwill and encouragement to come across more clearly.

Coming back again to the mother-in-law example above, you might continue the correction by saying something like:

'I can say this to you because I know you would never want to undermine me and because you have been so supportive in the past - for example last month when I had 'flu - I don't know what I would have done without you.'

This compliment is specific and brief. It needs to be sincere too, of course - a compliment should never be used to manipulate people. Ending with a word of encouragement is the most surprising, and probably the most revolutionary thing, about giving corrections assertively. It can make all the difference to how a correction is received. It has been shown to work well for correcting people in a work environment, but it is really effective too in a family setting.

How long does it take?

A correction need only take a minute - or much less. It can be as simple and short as: 'That means that you've just told me a lie. I'm disappointed, because you don't usually tell lies.' Or: 'My child hasn't had any homework for the past week, and I'm not happy with that - though I also have to say that he's happy in class and loves you as a teacher.'

Can you see how these examples meet the guidelines we have just been looking at?

Of course, corrections will not always be so simple. They may take longer. Feel free to be quite flexible - not necessarily to follow the structure we have just been looking at. You may feel the need to ask questions about the behaviour, for example. Very often, someone being corrected will also need a chance to give an explanation. If so, it may be important to listen for new information and give them a sense of being understood ('I didn't know about this.. That must have been hard for you..')

Or a correction may call for some negotiation about what changes may now be necessary so that both people can have their needs met as far as possible. Also negotiation about what consequences will apply if the agreement is ignored. It often helps to write down what has been agreed, as people's memories of that can be quite different and could cause further dispute. And it may also be helpful to arrange a time for reviewing how things are working out in practice.

Another reason why a correction may take longer is that the person being corrected may be quite uncooperative. If you are not being listened to or respected, you may have to use 'broken record', repeating again and again what it is specifically that you need or want, but avoiding aggression in your tone of voice. 'I hear what you're saying, but I need...'

Summing up

To sum up. In this chapter we have looked at four guidelines for giving corrections. The first is to choose an appropriate time. You can be much more effective when tempers have cooled down, and the other person is then more open to listening to you.

Secondly, be specific. In talking to your boss,

I'm disappointed, because you don't usually tell lies.

for example, it won't help to say 'You're a bully' or 'You're the rudest man I have ever met' but something direct and specific like: 'This morning you corrected me in front of three other people.'

The third guideline is to speak personally. Not 'You better stop bullying me around.', which is a You-message - though you may feel angry and want to say aggressive things like that. Better to say: 'I felt humiliated and angry. If you want to correct me, I have a right to be corrected privately.'

Then encourage. It may be the last thing you feel like doing, but it can make all the difference. Be specific and sincere in what you say: 'I know you weren't attacking me personally, of course. In fact, I like working here, because there's a friendly atmosphere and I'm usually treated with respect.'

Needless to say, corrections like this will not come naturally off the tip of your tongue. They will take a bit of practice and will usually need to be prepared in advance — especially the positive ending. They may sound stilted and awkward at first - and you will be ineffective if you try using this method too often - but it does pay to reflect before giving a constructive criticism.

Such reflection may mean that you will give fewer corrections, of course, but that will be no harm — we tend to give far too many, anyway. And what you do say will certainly be more effective and more useful for building up the people around you instead of tearing them down.

I can say this to you because I know you would never want to undermine me......

GETTING IN TOUCH SESSION FOUR

Take a minute or so to think of at least one situation where *you* may need to give constructive criticism to a family member, friend, neighbour, someone in a community group you belong to, or at your work. Here are some typical examples which may help to get you in touch:

1. Your daughter/son doesn't do the household chore that has been agreed upon.

2. Your partner/child leaves soiled clothes scattered on the bedroom floor.

3. You have discovered that your mother, who lives with you, has been saying critical things to your brothers and sisters about your lifestyle (going out too much!) and your parenting methods.

4. Your boss is a bully, makes all the decisions for you, and is quite aggressive when you don't do things exactly as you're told.

5. The stereo in your son's bedroom can be heard all over the house.

6. Your sister regularly borrows things from you and doesn't return them.

7. The children next door have begun to take a shortcut to the shop by going through your garden, often trampling on plants.

8. Your friend talks non-stop, and frequently interrupts you as soon as you start to speak.

9. Two of your children are constantly squabbling, screaming and aggressive with one another.

10. One man you drink with regularly will often let you buy him a drink but seldom offers to buy *you* a drink.

In pairs talk about how you normally deal with this situation?

TABLE FOUR: GIVING CONSTRUCTIVE CRITICISM

Here are four guidelines for correcting people in a way that helps to build them up and enable them to make the necessary changes. Which of the guidelines do you find easiest, and which is the most difficult one?

1. CHOOSE A SUITABLE TIME

Correction on the spot is often not appropriate.

'I need to talk to you. Is this a good time? . . . .'

2. BE SPECIFIC

Talk about a current problem — no old sores! Limit the correction to only one problem at a time, and give specific examples of the behaviour.

'On Monday and Wednesday, you weren't in bed until after 10.30'.

3. SPEAK PERSONALLY

Express your thoughts, feelings, needs, etc. as your own.

'I was quite disappointed that you didn't keep to your agreement. It's important to me that you get your sleep and are not too tired for school'.

4. ENCOURAGE

Acknowledge the person as good, cared about, valued, well-intentioned. But don't talk generally — be specific, or you may sound patronising. And it helps a lot to keep 'catching' the person doing better.

'I know, or course, that you don't mean to upset me, because there were special circumstances this week'.

37

COMMENTS FROM PARENTS

I was trying to get served at an ice-cream counter, and the assistant was serving the pushiest people. I felt so frustrated, but I dreaded making a fuss. Eventually I said: 'There are two children there and they were waiting to be served before I came.' She served them - and me next! Maybe it was a cop out - it sounded less selfish to stand up for someone else's rights, but you did say to start with small things that were possible.

I'm amazed, after all these years, to find that it's possible to be calmer and more respectful when correcting the children. It doesn't just work better - it gives *me* peace of mind too.

Our biggest success was in weaning our two year old, Aidan, off the bottle. He had us up five times during the night to get him a bottle. He cried for a long time to get us to change our minds, but we stayed firm. It's great freedom.

I've always been one of those people who would do anything for anyone except for myself! I couldn't cope with all the demands, but I couldn't ask for help - yet I'd feel hurt that my family couldn't see for themselves what I needed. The course is helping me to be direct and to ask for help. My husband is doing the shopping now and he says he actually enjoys it.

I needed to do something about Kathy screaming at her two brothers every time they came into her room. I pointed out that she had a perfect right to privacy, but that her screaming left me feeling sad - for her as well as for her brothers - and I reminded her of how much better she had handled this situation a few times when she had stayed calm. She talked about her anger first and got some of that off her chest, then we ended up role-playing the situation as

we do during the sessions here. I was one of her brothers and she was brilliant at claiming her rights without getting angry. She was excited at how simple it all was, and fascinated that to shout and be aggressive was to lose a fight. 'This is like a game you learn from, Mum,' she said, 'Will you do it with me at other times?' That gives me hope - to have a way of helping my children to learn to be assertive instead of being aggressive.

I hate him smoking in the house, but he's eighty years old and I love him, and I know he wouldn't understand if I made an issue of it. I'm not going to hurt him. So I'm choosing to live with something I hate because the alternative is much worse. And I think that's assertive.

Looking back over the course and how I got on between sessions, I think the session on giving criticism has had the biggest impact on me.

David always resents correction and turns back on me like a weasel. So it was interesting to see how saying something positive at the end almost took the rug from under his feet. He didn't say anything, just nodded and accepted.

It's interesting what the book says about awareness being the key. I wasn't aware until this past week that I say 'sorry' so much. Don't get me wrong - I think it's important to be able to say sorry to the children when you've done wrong, but in this case I know I haven't done wrong amd I'm just being apologetic instead of assertive.

I tend to be a shouter. That's my way of correcting. I know it's stupid, but it's like a bad habit that you fall back on without thinking.

CASE STUDIES/SKILL PRACTICE

Form groups of three, and take some time to decide how you might give constructive criticism in some of the situations in the 'Getting in Touch' section - or in another situation that you personally need to deal with. Talk it out first, then practise it, using the four steps in Table Four. For example, in the first situation, you might say:

(SPECIFIC) - 'For the past two days, you cleared off after the evening meal without doing the wash-up as you had agreed'.

(PERSONAL) - 'I was left on my own to clear up, after having prepared the meal, so I felt quite taken for granted - I had a sense of being treated like a maid. I just need you to do your chore without being reminded'.

(ENCOURAGE) - 'I must say I find it's a great help when you do the wash-up without being reminded - I feel really encouraged, and it helps the whole atmosphere of the house.'

Allow each person to have a turn correcting, being corrected, and observing. Take time to say how you felt and to listen to comments on how you came across before moving on to a different person and a different situation each time. If everyone has had a turn, you may like to try a more difficult situation where the person being corrected needs to explain or argues back.

PLANNING FOR NEXT WEEK

When you were doing the 'Getting in touch' exercise, you were asked to decide on one person whom you need to correct. Over the next twenty four hours, you might try taking that person aside for constructive criticism. Practise giving constructive criticisms a few times during the week - and look for at least one opportunity to be assertive each day.

It is also suggested that you take a little time each evening to relax your body and mind and become *aware* of when you criticised poorly - for example without encouraging or without

being specific - and when you criticised constructively, speaking personally, encouraging, etc. Then foresee how you will act in one situation you will be meeting the following day. Notice how you normally act, and then see yourself acting assertively - with love and self-control. Note little details like your surroundings and what you'll be wearing - the more vividly you see it all, the more likely you are to be assertive. Pay particular attention to your tone of voice. Such awareness can be the key to effective change.

1. When will I take time each day to become aware and to foresee my behaviour?

_____

2. What situations will I deal with/ who/ when/ where?.. What I'll try... What body language do I need to be careful about? Feel free to talk this out with the person beside you.

_____

CHAPTER FIVE: ENCOURAGEMENT AND ASSERTIVENESS

An oppressed reaction

Tina: 'You're looking well. I like your sweater.'

Denise: (embarrassed, and casting her eyes around in discomfort) 'Oh, I just put on the first thing I could find.'

Tina: 'But I really like it on you!'

Denise: 'This old thing? I've had it for years... But *you're* looking terrific...'

Poor Denise finds it difficult to accept a compliment. She feels so uncomfortable with a compliment that she rushes to dismiss it. Then, when Tina attempts to reassure her, Denise contines to put herself down and desperately attempts to focus attention off herself on to her friend.

Does it sound familiar? Sadly, the inability to accept compliments is very common. Many of us, when we receive a compliment, rush to shrug it off (You must be joking!), or we put ourselves down ('I'm not much good at it really!'), or we make a joke, or go into long explanations and excuses that show how uncomfortable we feel. Or, like Denise, we quickly turn the spotlight onto somebody else. When someone suggests that we might be doing a good job as parents, we say something like 'You're a much better parent than I'll ever be!' or 'If you saw me ten minutes ago!' or 'If you only knew the truth!'

The truth about yourself

The trouble is that many people are convinced that the truth isn't very flattering, that they're not doing a good job, that they're not really very nice people to know. And that is not true. The truth is that you are a much better person than you believe yourself to be. Have you ever noticed how easy it is to accuse yourself of being lazy or selfish even though you are lazy or selfish only *some* of the time - yet you will not accept that you are a good parent or hard-working or generous if you only have *these* qualities some of the time? A virtue needs to be almost one hundred percent present before we accept it in ourselves, but a vice only needs to be ten percent present to be accepted as true. It is a double standard. We live by two different standards a great deal of the time - so that we seldom appreciate our goodness, we constantly live with a critical voice whispering in our ears, and we react to compliments in ways that are passive or oppressed. It is really sad that we put ourselves down like this.

Oh, I just put on the first thing I could find.

Aggressive reactions

And don't be fooled by aggressive reactions to compliments either. It is the same mentality of low self-esteem and lack of a true appreciation of self that reacts to compliments with sarcasm or a blunt contradiction - 'What do you know!' 'Don't be stupid - any fool can do that!' or 'Yeah. I heard that before!' People don't usually mean to hurt you when they say things like this - they are just reacting desperately, terrified of letting the truth in to contradict a poor self-image.

Boasting, incidentally, is another aggressive reaction that many young boys use to cover over their feelings of insecurity by adopting a macho image 'Yeah. Out of my way, everybody. I'm the best.' Unfortunately, a macho act can stick, and it quickly becomes second nature.

Unfortunate effects

You will notice, of course, that oppressed or passive reactions are much more common than aggressive ones, especially among friends and acquaintances, but aggressive, put-down reactions ('What would you know!'/ 'Says who!'/ 'What are *you* looking for?') are all too common among family members.

Such reactions to compliments are unfortunate. **By not letting in the light of other people's good opinions of us, we condemn ourselves to living in the darkness of self-doubt and low self-respect - and we can never be properly**

assertive until we respect ourselves. There is nothing either assertive or humble in cowering from the truth.

Letting compliments in

How, then, do you become more assertive in accepting compliments? It is not difficult, although it may take some practice. You look directly at the person and thank them *briefly* and *simply* ('Thank you. It's nice to hear that'), or you agree with the compliment, expressing a positive feeling ('Thank you. I was quite happy with it myself.')

This approach has two considerable advantages. First, it lets the compliment in. Instead of shrugging it off, you let it penetrate your defences. And that begins to build your self-image and increase your self-respect.

A second advantage is that you help the other person to feel good by accepting their compliment as a gift. After all, it is frustrating to have a gift thrown back in one's face, whereas it can be really encouraging to be able to put a smile into someone's eyes. If, instead of saying 'You're much better at it!' you say 'Thank you. that's one of the nicest things anyone has said to me in a long time!' or 'Thanks. I find it really encouraging to hear that!' then the person giving the compliment is *also* encouraged.

In the United States many children are trained by their parents to look at people and say 'thank you' for a compliment - just as they are trained to say 'thank you' when someone gives them a

Don't be stupid - any fool can do that!

gift or passes the milk. Initially their 'thank you' may be quite automatic and may mean little, but it does gradually affect the way they see themselves. People often comment on how graciously young children in the United States tend to accept compliments - with a clear, direct look and an easy 'thank you' that indicates a healthy belief in themselves and a good self-image. The benefits of dropping barriers and letting in the good opinions of others can be considerable.

'But they don't mean it!'

Now, that is all very well if a compliment is sincere. What should you do, however, if you suspect that people are saying flattering things to you that they do not mean?

But how do you know that a compliment is insincere? Be wary of making that judgement. Isn't it possible that that is part of the double standard we have just been talking about whereby we refuse to believe good things about ourselves but accept our own negative judgements to be correct! Moreover, even if someone is insincere in what they say, why should that make *you* less sincere or ungracious? Why should you let someone else make you cringe or act in an oppressed - or aggressive - way? You can still be assertive and accept a compliment graciously. If you cannot honestly agree 'Thanks, Mary, I was happy with the way it turned out.' you can at least agree in part 'Thanks, Mary, I was pretty happy with it.'

'I'd be like a robot!'

Another objection is raised by people who react to saying a robot-like, automatic 'thank you' to every compliment. But you are not a robot, and you have the freedom to thank people just as you have the freedom to develop any other good habit. What's so bad about having some polite, courteous habits? You don't *have* to say thanks, of course. With some friends, depending on the context, a perfect reaction may be to banter with them, even to tell them to go and see a psychiatrist! But do be careful - there is a difference between good-humoured banter and the type of joking that attempts to cover up the discomfort you feel at letting in the truth about your own goodness. It can be helpful to get feedback occasionally from a good friend on whether they see you reacting to compliments or accepting them.

Giving compliments is assertive

So much for receiving compliments. Giving compliments and encouraging people is also an area that calls for assertiveness. Yet, the passive approach is to think of all kinds of reasons why you shouldn't tell others about the good impressions you have of them - 'They'd think it strange if I said something nice to them.' 'They might wonder what I was looking for.' 'I'll just do what everyone else does and drift along, so that nobody notices me or thinks me odd.'

Aggressive attitudes are even more crippling - people who tend to act aggressively often find it difficult to say something encouraging. They usually want a fight. They'll get their rights by hook or by crook. They want to win, which means that the other has to be beaten, has to be criticised rather than complimented. It is unfortunate that this hard, tough attitude is often confused with assertiveness.

For assertiveness is not just about standing up for your rights and sharing your negative feelings with others; it also includes telling people about the good you see in them, and how it has impressed or touched you. We have seen that the assertive approach is to express your thoughts and feelings openly with your family and friends - but expressing your *positive* feelings and impressions is an important part of that. 'I like that colour on you.' 'I love you.' 'I'm happy with the way you did that.'

How to give compliments that strike home

Expressing these positive feelings can also make a compliment more effective and help it strike home. For a good compliment will usually include feelings and be *personal*. Many sincere compliments are not effective simply because they are not personal. They use 'you' instead of 'I'. They say 'You're wonderful!' - instead of 'I like the way you get along with people.' Or 'You're a great driver' - instead of 'I feel relaxed when you're driving.' **Expressing our positive feelings is a powerful way to build up our children and those we come into contact with.**

Another thing that helps a compliment to strike home and build someone up is to make it *specific*. You can say 'You're wonderful' about anyone, but when you say 'I was watching how you handled that situation, and I'm impressed - you looked directly at him and didn't lose your cool', that will come across as much more sincere because it is specific. When you say something general to your daughter, like 'You're a very good girl.' she may or may not find that helpful, but when you say 'Thanks for that cup of tea. I'm pleased that you made it without being asked,' she will have a much clearer sense of being noticed and appreciated.

People who are familiar with our parenting programmes will already be aware of the distinction made between praise, (which may not be helpful), and encouragement, (which does tend to build people up). It may help to think of praise as something general and impersonal, whereas genuine encouragement is usually specific and personal, as in the examples above.

Positive body language

As with all assertive skills, of course, something is missing from any compliment if you are looking at your shoes as you talk. Your body language needs to match what you are saying. To be assertive, it helps to look straight at the person you are giving a compliment to and to speak calmly, without an apologetic stammer or long-winded explanation.

It's not just a matter of how things are *said*, of course - encouragement goes away beyond words. It's more a question of *thinking* positively. And **positive thinkers usually find it easier to express what they feel in an affectionate nod, a smile, a readiness to listen to you, a hug, even a gentle touch that is aware of you, or an understanding grunt. These are particularly important things for a parent.**

Such things cannot be faked, but they can be developed when you replace critical, negative thoughts ('She acts as if she owned the place.' 'He's got nine spellings wrong out of twenty.') with understanding or positive thoughts ('She's lonely.' 'He's got eleven spellings right out of twenty.')

But there's nothing to praise!

But what do you do if you can find nothing good to comment on? What if a family member or workmate is extremely rude and disrespectful?

You look directly at the person and thank them briefly...

Well, as we have seen, there are other assertive skills for dealing with disrespect or put-downs. You're not expected to make yourself a doormat or to attempt to offer a compliment to someone who has just humiliated you. When people are very negative and uncooperative, though, it can also help to remember that they are probably in a good deal of pain. You can usually help by zoning in on something positive - like telling the attention-seeking child. 'It was nice how you let me get on with things this morning. I was glad to be able to chat with Margaret when she came in.'

In some cases, however, the truth is that **many of us do not *notice* the good in others because we are not used to looking for it.** The same dark glasses that prevent us from seeing the good in ourselves will often prevent us from seeing it in others too. Many children can identify with the old saying: 'When I do something right, nobody ever remembers; when I do something wrong, nobody ever forgets.'

Everyone has good qualities. At the end of any day, each one of us can look back and think of a number of times when we ourselves have made an effort or acted responsibly or kindly. The same is true for others. They also are making an effort. The good is there - if we look for it. Instead of looking for 'perfection', concentrating on the flaws and trying to catch our children doing wrong, we can do wonderful things when we think positively and practise catching them doing things well - even catching them making a little effort or showing a small improvement. Regularly noticing something positive goes a long way towards building people up and improving their self-image.

Four to one

Here is a sobering thought to finish with. Some researchers have come up with an interesting finding. They found that, in order to come across as a positive, supportive person, with whom people normally feel safe and trusting, **you need to say or do *four* sincere, positive things for every negative one!** These 'positive things' don't have to be compliments - it may be something as simple as a touch or a smile, an unexpected present or a thoughtful cup of tea. That is part of the challenge and the invitation to be assertive.

To say or do four sincere, positive things for every negative one.

GETTING IN TOUCH SESSION FIVE

Here are some ways of reacting to compliments. Take a minute to look over them. Do you sometimes make similar comments when you're complimented? Tick any that apply:

PASSIVE (Common reaction when with friends)

✓● **Don't let it in, shrug it off.** Did you think so? I wasn't too happy with it myself.'

● **Make a joke.** 'You want my autograph?

● **Put self down.** 'If you saw me at home with my own children!'

✓● **Turn spotlight off self by complimenting someone else.** 'I don't know - you're much better than me at it.'

✓● **Go into long explanations**

AGGRESSIVE (Also common with partners and family)

● **Contradict other's judgement.** 'Don't be silly! Anyone can do that!'

? ● **Attack the other's motives.** What are you looking for!

● **Sarcasm.** 'Oh. You've noticed me at last.'

● **Reject compliment dismissively.** 'How would you know!'

● **Boast.** 'Yeah. I always get placed in the top three.'

In pairs talk about what you normally say and feel when you reject a compliment? Why do you think that is?

43

TABLE FIVE: GIVING AND RECEIVING COMPLIMENTS

You are not expected to use all of the guidelines below in any given situation. Choose what you feel is appropriate.

SOME WAYS OF RECEIVING COMPLIMENTS

LOOK OPENLY AND DIRECTLY AT THE PERSON — Not at the ground

THANK THE PERSON — AND EXPRESS A POSITIVE FEELING — 'Thanks, Sandra, I'm glad you liked it. / Thank you, Joe, I'm pleased you told me that. / Thanks, it really helps me to hear that'.

AGREE WITH THE COMPLIMENT — 'Thanks, Alan, I was happy with the way it turned out.' (If you cannot honestly agree, then agree in part, 'Thanks, I was pretty happy with it.').

KEEP YOUR REPLY SHORT — a long reply, with explanations or excuses shows your lack of ease with the compliment and prevents you from letting it in.

GUIDELINES FOR GIVING COMPLIMENTS

LOOK OPENLY AND DIRECTLY AT THE PERSON and speak simply, without stammering or hesitation.

CATCH PEOPLE DOING RIGHT — To do this, it helps to think positively about people, not looking for excellence — just for some effort, or a little improvement, or co-operation, or something you *like.* 'That was a good help to me — thanks a lot'. 'Thanks for doing your chore — the place looks a lot tidier'.

BE SPECIFIC AND BRIEF — Avoid generalities like 'You're great / you're very good'. Point out specifically what behaviour you liked. 'You didn't raise your voice with him — I was impressed at how calm you stayed'. 'Last week you couldn't manage that at all, but you've hardly missed a note.'

USE 'I' 'I liked . .' 'I was happy about . . .' 'I feel relaxed and safe with you when you're driving . .' 'I was impressed with the way you . . .' 'I'm delighted you did that . .' 'I feel encouraged by the progress you've made . . .' 'Well done, I thought you handled him well — he can be difficult to deal with'.

BE SINCERE — A compliment should always be truthful. Avoid flattery or exaggeration.

COMMENTS FROM PARENTS

I know I'm quite assertive, but what I'm beginning to realise is that I'm assertive in some ways, and the opposite in other ways. It's sobering to realise how poor I am at encouraging people and letting them know the good I see in them.

I love that idea of 'catching' people doing good. It is just the opposite to how we have been trained.

My husband was away for the weekend and I started off great, telling the children what a great help they were and so on. But by Sunday evening I had no energy left and I found myself blaming and saying the most horrible things to the children. It's awful when you're tired and under pressure how you fall back on the same old reactions.

I haven't gone out of my way to think up compliments, but I'm not taking the family for granted as I did - I notice the little things they do and I say 'thank you'.

It really hit me when I heard that you have to give four times as many compliments as corrections so that the children can experience you as a positive person. That's what has had the biggest effect on me.

You could see from her body language, the hands in the pocket, the shoulder against the wall, that she was on the defensive and going to be 'tough'. But the compliment at the end floored her. The hands came out of the pockets, she looked taken aback, and she actually apologised!

I was glowing after what Geraldine said about me. I knew she was speaking sincerely, and it was encouraging that she saw me like that. I'd like to be able to build up my children in the same way.

I took one of the girls aside and told her how much I liked having her in my class because of the interest she showed. I said I felt encouraged when I looked around the class and saw the open, listening expression on her face. But I think I said too much - I embarrassed her, I think, and made her self-conscious so that she actually finds it hard now to make eye-contact with me!

I have a great sense of every one of us being in the same boat. I love hearing your little stories about what happens in your family and the different ways you have of dealing with it. It's a relief to know we're all going through the same thing, and it gives me ideas for new approaches.

The danger is that you could become an expert on saying the right encouraging thing to your child, and you could miss the point that it's far more encouraging to a child to be taken aside and get a bit of special time, or play, or some listening.

The compliment at the end makes all the difference when I have to correct a member of staff - it keeps us friendly.

I think we put others down in the hope that they'll feel as bad about themselves as we feel about ourselves.

CASE STUDIES

Form groups of three, and try to think of common 'poor' compliments - especially those beginning with 'you' instead of 'I'. Notice how they are often patronising, too general, not specific, not personal, comparing to others. Here's a few to get you started 'You're wonderful!' 'You're doing a grand job, dear.' 'You're a great woman!'.

How do you feel when you receive a compliment like this?

Next, can you think of some poor *reactions* to compliments? (Check the 'Getting in Touch' section if necessary). Again, here are some to get you started: 'It's no big deal!' 'If you only knew the truth!' 'The meal? It was just thrown together!' 'This coat? I got it cheap in a sale!' 'My hair? Don't be daft - look at the state of it!'

SKILL PRACTICE

This is a chance to practise receiving compliments - which is where many people stop being assertive! In the following list, underline the six things that you most like about yourself. (Don't worry if they don't apply all the time - we're usually only too ready to admit faults like being selfish or bad-tempered, even though these *certainly* don't apply all the time!): **My hair; eyes; sense of fun; generous; thoughtful; sincere; good-humoured; sense of justice; honest; relaxed; reliable; friendly, responsible; patient; gentle; open; modest; good listener,**

Other qualities, abilities ...

_____

Ways I have grown recently

_____

Now form pairs, preferably with someone who knows you fairly well, swop sheets, and, using one of the underlined words at a time, say something like 'One of the things I like about you is that you're (generous).' The other person pauses to let the compliment sink in, and calmly replies something like: 'Thank you. I'm glad you told me that.' Resist the temptation to explain or talk too long. You may need to practise this a few times until you accept it sincerely - allow time for comments on your body language, tone of voice, facial expression, etc. Then switch roles - the other person gives the compliment and the first person responds calmly and assertively. Keep switching roles until all the words have been said. (These will not be perfect compliments because they are not *specific* but they are *truthful* in that you have accepted that you have these qualities.)

PLANNING FOR NEXT WEEK

Over the next week, (indeed, for the rest of your life!), you might try giving compliments at least once each day. The more you practise, the more the habit will become second nature to you. Decide who you will encourage in the next twenty four hours. Can you close your eyes and imagine yourself acting assertively, giving encouragement in the situation?

It is also suggested that you take a little time each evening this week to relax your body and mind and become *aware* of how you have been giving and receiving compliments, and then foresee how you will act in one situation you will be meeting the following day. Notice how you normally act, and then see yourself acting assertively - with love and self-control. Note little details like your surroundings and what you'll be wearing - the more vividly you see it all, the more likely you are to be assertive. This daily exercise can have a powerful effect in helping you make these skills your own in a natural way.

1. When will I take time each day to become aware and to foresee my behaviour? _____

2. Who in my family can I compliment in the next 24 hours? What have I liked about them, and how can I make what I say personal? What body language do I need to be careful about? Feel free to talk this out with the person beside you.

_____

CHAPTER SIX: A WAY OF LIFE

Mrs Carpenter was irritated. Two boys in their early teens were chattering away in the row behind her in the cinema. Things like that had irritated her before, but she hadn't ever done anything about them in the past. She liked to be 'nice' to people, even when they did not respect her rights. Anything for peace. Now she was learning to be assertive and she decided to ask for quiet. She turned around and looked directly at the noisiest of the boys. She knew it was important to establish eye-contact.

'Ssh' she said.

That was all. Low-key. No need to use a sledgehammer to crack a nut. And it did sober them. The chattering changed to whispers.

But the change only lasted for a minute or two. Then the chattering started again, and Mrs Carpenter knew she needed to be more assertive.

Again she turned around and established eye-contact. 'I need you to be quiet' she said. 'I can't concentrate on the film with your talking'. She kept eye-contact for a few seconds after speaking in order to let what she was saying register more fully.

Silence followed, interrupted only by a little muttering. The muttering increased, though, with some scoffing and disrespectful remarks as the boys began to put on a show of false bravado. 'Who does she think she is!' 'Must think she owns this place!'

Mrs Carpenter was angry now and felt aggressive. She didn't act on that, but she turned around and said:

'I'm annoyed that you've ignored what I said. If you continue to make noise, I'll report you to the management'.

The boys laughed in contempt, desperate now to bolster each other up and not to lose face in front of each other.

Mrs Carpenter was as good as her word. She got up and went for the supervisor. A minute later, two red-faced boys were being told to move to another part of the cinema and warned that they would be put outside if they made any more noise.

This is an example of different *stages* of assertiveness, moving from a gentle reminder to finally taking action. It is not always appropriate to tackle a situation like this, of course - in some circumstances it could even be dangerous! But very often, a gentle, low-key approach is all that is needed. Mrs Carpenter was probably unusual in that she met with rudeness and disrespect. But this sometimes happens, and then assertive

I need you to be quiet

communication is not enough. Action may be called for.

A way of life

For **assertiveness, properly understood, is more than communication; it includes taking action.** It is part of a freer and more open lifestyle - a lifestyle not cramped by inhibitions or aggressive habits or fears of what people might think. It is more a way of life than a set of skills. It is about how we live our lives.

Life is to be enjoyed. Relationships are to be enjoyed. Family life is to be enjoyed. **Assertiveness calls us to stop drifting along, existing, merely coping, to take greater control of our lives, to move out of the ruts we have got into and to enjoy living.** Maybe that means getting out more often to a park and just noticing the trees and the birds and the sky. Maybe it's a question of joining a club or organisation - for exercise, or for a better social life, or to help disadvantaged people. Maybe it's a matter of planning more fun with your children. Or you may want to develop yourself, to read more, to meditate, or learn a musical instrument, or join an evening class. There is a list of things you may like to do - or stop doing! - in the Planning section at the end of this chapter. You can never do all the things you'd like to do, of course, but it may be a good idea to look over that list from time to time and ask yourself how you're doing.

It's all a bit selfish!

But is this emphasis not all a bit selfish - to be so concerned with getting *my* rights and claiming *my* space and doing things *I* enjoy?

No. Assertiveness, properly understood, encourages me to respect myself and *others,* and to enable others to claim *their* needs and live a more fulfilled life too. That will mean a certain amount of negotiating and settling for *less* than I might want. We have already seen that people who act assertively will not always get what they want.

But we do *need* to be reminded not to neglect ourselves and our own needs. In the past, far too many people tended to neglect themselves - often in the name of religion. **Assertiveness has not been seen as something that is a great asset to a fuller, more whole and more spiritual life - an approach to life that is neither violent nor aggressive nor passive nor dishonest.** A way of relating to people that is direct and honest and free and open. A *means* to a 'more abundant' life.

Getting out more often to a park

A clearer picture
There is a strong temptation, of course, to settle for the way you've always done things - to brush your feelings under the carpet, to smile and pretend that all is well - rather than risk conflict with your teenage daughter, your friend, your husband. People are even praised in our society for this kind of dishonesty. Husbands and wives are praised for 'staying together' when the truth may be that they have been burying their tensions for years, their communication on the feeling level has almost stopped, and their marriage is as good as dead. **Assertiveness offers hope that a relationship can be real again.** Let's review how that happens by taking

a little time now to review the various skills we have met and see how they all fit together.

Assertiveness includes a whole variety of skills - making requests, dealing with requests from others, expressing your needs, feelings, ideas, giving constructive criticism, dealing with criticism that is directed at you, giving compliments, receiving compliments - and now taking action! What is it that ties together such different skills under one heading?

Openly expressing yourself
Perhaps the key word is respect. Respect for yourself and for others. That is why aggressive or dishonest behaviour (which does not respect others) is not assertive. That is why passive, oppressed behaviour (which does not respect yourself) is not assertive either. **Assertiveness is about respect, and it shows itself in communication and behaviour that is increasingly open and free.**

That word 'open' is crucial. Being direct and honest and open in how you express yourself, without aggression or apology. Open in expressing your feelings ('I'm disappointed' 'I feel sad that you didn't include him.'). Open in expressing your needs ('I need time to think about this.' 'I need a rest.'). Open with your requests ('I would like you not to smoke in here' 'Can I have a glass of water please.'). Open about your beliefs ('I believe that having sex is a commitment for life.' 'I believe people should be free to choose'). Open about your opinions ('I support the Labour Party.' 'I think capital punishment is right/wrong.'). This openness is not just about your negative opinions and

I would like you not to smoke in here

48

feelings, of course, but about your positive ones too, so it includes compliments as well as corrections ('I'm surprised at how well you've done that.' 'I like the calm way you corrected him - you were firm without being harsh.')

All this often involves taking a risk, making yourself vulnerable, particularly when your beliefs or ideas are unpopular or when others may judge your feelings to be unacceptable.

Open to requests or criticisms

Another aspect of this openness is in the way you deal with requests or criticisms coming at you from others. Instead of an unthinking 'yes' or 'no' to requests, instead of passively accepting criticisms or agreeing to requests out of weakness, or instead of an aggressive rebuff because you feel threatened, assertiveness encourages you to be thoughtful and open when you meet with requests, demands, or criticisms.

You begin with an openness to listening as you ask questions (What do you want the money for? Why do you say that I'm unfair?). Then you can say you need time, if you do need time, for that is one of your rights ('I'll need time to think this over.' 'I'll come back to you when I've had a chance to consider it.') When you do come back, you may need to be open to negotiating a little, ('I wonder how we can meet each other's needs in this situation?..') Your response then can be a clear, direct acceptance/ agreement, or a firm but gentle refusal/ denial ('No, I'm not responsible for the mistake.' 'Yes, you may go to bed a half-hour later, provided you get up at...')

A 'no' will not always be accepted respectfully, of course, so you may need to use 'broken record' firmly and calmly ('Yes, I can hear what you're saying, but I'm not responsible for the mistake...')

Openness in criticising or confronting

Openness is also crucial when you need to correct or challenge someone's behaviour. It is important to be very specific in pointing out what is wrong, but the correction will come across much more powerfully when you are also open about how you feel ('You've done that three times since we began our dinner, and I find it disgusting - it offends me.' 'You brought your friends through the kitchen but none of you spoke to me. I was surprised, and a bit shocked, at being ignored like that.')

A correction is much more effective when you end with a compliment, mentioning your positive opinions or feelings. ('I'm quite sure you didn't

mean to treat me like a servant - I usually feel respected by you.' or 'I'm telling you this because I'm impressed at how open you usually are to being told things like this.')

When someone refuses to talk...

The effect of treating people with respect and openness has to be experienced to be believed, for assertive skills cut through the pretences and barriers that destroy relationships. Take, for example, a very common form of non-communication - when a friend or a member of your family goes off in a huff, avoids you, or refuses to talk. Perhaps you need to let some cooling down time go by first, as they probably feel misunderstood and angry. Then you move in, not to confront them with indignation ('What *is* wrong with you!' 'When are you going to stop acting like a baby!') but with respect and openness. It may not help to say 'We have to talk!' That could be offputting or threatening. Better to be open and personal, using 'I' rather than 'we' - 'I'd like a chat.' That may be all that is needed. If they hedge, or are not co-operative, ('There's no point in talking any more'), you can then make a stronger statement, but keep it personal - you might say 'I *need* a chat with you.' Your openness and directness will usually break down the resistance.

Will I be different?

But don't let yourself get discouraged if you read this and think 'When I read these examples, I nod my head, and I'd love to be more

Yes, you may go to bed a half-hour later, provided...

I need a chat with you

family meeting, or plan an outing. Tell someone who is abusing your rights that you need to talk to them. Plan to do something you'll enjoy - even for the sake of your own children (you'll have more to give them when you're looking after yourself!) Discover your own power and freedom and self-respect, and your life will become more fulfilling, more reflective and more rewarding, and **your family will learn respect in the best possible way - by experiencing it and seeing it in your home.**

assertive, but I'm never able to think of the right things to say. In an everyday situation, I'm a million miles away from that!'

That's perfectly normal. At the end of an assertiveness course, you are only beginning. But the difference lies in your *awareness*. You are more aware of assertiveness now, of what it is and what it isn't. Including the fundamental belief of those who teach assertiveness that **you cannot change others; you can only change yourself.** Awareness is the first step in making a change. Indeed, it is strongly recommended that you take a little time each evening just to become aware of how you have used (and failed to use) assertive skills that day. That daily awareness may not bring immediate change, but it can be remarkably effective over a period of time.

Another thing that can help a lot is to find someone with whom you can sit down to talk out and then role-play before any difficult situation you have to deal with. Practise dealing with the situation a number of times, getting feedback each time until you know you are coming across assertively. That will normally give you great confidence in dealing with any situation.

So break out of the rut. Enjoy your parenting, your friends, your work, your leisure, yourself. And help others to enjoy life. Assertiveness enables you to do that. Begin by taking small risks. **Stop listening to old whispers in your ear about things being hopeless - contradict them.** Plan more. Begin to break that addiction (to work, or nagging, or tobacco, or whatever) that is crippling you, leaving you unfree, and doing violence to yourself and your family. Stop waiting for things to happen - make the first move. The more choices you make, the more you'll like yourself. Take initiatives. Set up a

So break out of the rut......

TABLE SIX: ASSERTIVE SKILLS

*This is a summary of the principal assertive skills that we have met during the course. They are under three main headings, but these divisions are not rigid — if your child is hostile and un-cooperative, for example, approaches two **and** three may be appropriate. Bear in mind, too, that being assertive is more than mere communication — it also involves taking action (and doing things you enjoy!) Where do you think you have improved, and where do you find most difficulty?*

1. OPENLY EXPRESSING YOUR OPINIONS, FEELINGS, NEEDS, REQUESTS, COMPLIMENTS.

- BE BRIEF, **DIRECT**, CLEAR, AND SPECIFIC

- SPEAK **PERSONALLY**

- LOOK DIRECTLY AT THE PERSON, STAY **CALM**, NO APOLOGY

2. DEALING OPENLY WITH REQUESTS OR CRITICISM

- ASK OPEN **QUESTIONS**

- YOU MAY NEED **TIME**

- THEN GIVE YOUR RESPONSE DIRECTLY, **FIRMLY**, GENTLY.

- USE **'BROKEN RECORD'** IF YOU'RE NOT BEING RESPECTED.

3. OPENLY GIVING CRITICISM OR CONFRONTING INJUSTICE

- BE BRIEF, CLEAR AND **SPECIFIC**

- MENTION THE **EFFECT** (INCLUDING YOUR FEELINGS)

- END WITH A SPECIFIC SINCERE **COMPLIMENT**

Which of the skills above do you have most difficulty with? Can you give an example?

COMMENTS FROM PARENTS

Now I'm taking thirty minutes a day just for me. I don't even answer the phone. I relax or read or whatever I feel like.

I can't put my finger on how I've changed, but I have. It's become part of me without me even being conscious of it. My horizons have widened. I know now there are other ways of handling situations.

I'm more aware that I have rights and needs. The session that helped me most was 'giving correction'. I find it difficult to give compliments.

I'm not letting my in-laws control me the way they did. I was afraid of them. All these years I've let Joe's father sit beside him in the front of the car. I didn't think I had a choice. Now I sit in the front. That may seem a small thing, but it's not small for me. And yesterday I told my mother-in-law not to prevent the child from crying, to let him cry. She didn't even object. We have the power to change the way things are when we decide to.

I know some people liked the Reflections at the end of the evening, but I found them a bit preachy.

I've never liked discussions or working in groups. The course has overcome my fear of them. I felt very at home and relaxed. But role-play is hard for me. I can see the benefit of it, but I don't like it.

It wasn't long enough. Maybe it was easier for the people who had practised some of these things already in a parenting programme, but it wasn't enough for me - there was too much to take in. We would also have needed two hours for a session instead of an hour and a half.

I would have liked more tips on dealing with adults who are close family members.

It was so easy to understand. Simple steps, well explained. Just what I needed. And a great bunch of people. I don't know what I'm going to do now on Monday evenings.

I'd have liked an introductory activity before getting down to business - just to offload some of the baggage I was carrying from home.

I'm no actress, but I was surprised, as the evenings went on, at how at ease I became with the role-play. And I learned a lot from it.

For the past number of weeks I feel better about myself. It must be because of the group support and feeling freer to be myself and not having anything to hide.

When I came on the course, I expected it would make me tougher. I know that was wrong now. But the thing that has helped me most was meeting Madeline and seeing how well her gentle approach works - she softens people and makes them gentler. No matter how angry I was, I would soften if I was treated the way she treats people.

For years I've been looking for something that was missing in myself and my parenting and my life, but I couldn't put my finger on what it was that was missing. I know now what was missing - really *loving* my children. I certainly didn't expect to find that on an assertiveness course.

CASE STUDIES/SKILL PRACTICE

This is a chance to revise and practise a variety of assertive skills. Take a minute or so to read down through this list and tick off a few examples that remind you of situations that you'd like to deal with assertively in your own life.

Then, form groups of three. Decide who will be acting assertively, who the observer will be, and who the third person will be for one of these situations. Before acting it out, you may like to talk briefly about the approach you will take, consulting Table Six if necessary. Before moving on to another situation and switching roles, take time, as usual, for feedback. You'll be coming back to these situations again next week, so don't worry if you feel there's too much here.

EXPRESSING OPINIONS, FEELINGS, NEEDS, REQUESTS, COMPLIMENTS..

● The people behind you in the cinema are quite noisy.

● You want to ask for a rise in wages.

● A busy consultant is dismissing you, but you want to ask him some questions about your medical complaint.

● Tension has arisen between you and your friend because of a misunderstanding. She has avoided you for the past few days.

● Your parents expect you to spend Christmas with them as usual. You want to spend Christmas at home.

● You end up doing most of the chores at home. You want to ask everyone to do a fair share.

● What have you noticed during the past week that you'd like to compliment someone on? How would you express it?

DEALING WITH REQUESTS OR CRITICISM

● Your twelve year old asks can he stay up late to watch the horror film - or a video which you consider unsuitable.

● Your supervisor asks you to work overtime, which doesn't suit.

● A friend (or one of your children!) who is quite insensitive says: 'You're hair looks awful and you're too fat!'

● Your sixteen year old daughter asks to go to an over-eighteens disco. When you say you're not happy about it, she says you're old-fashioned and out of touch.

● Your wife/husband says you don't care about the children - it's all left up to her/him.

GIVING CONSTRUCTIVE CRITICISM/ CONFRONTING

● The plates your son cleaned are still quite greasy.

● Your daughter has been using the telephone too much recently.

● Your mother-in-law spoils the children.

● Your builder is working on five other jobs as well as yours and trying to keep everyone happy. You are dissatisfied.

● Your frequently correct your child in an aggressive tone.

● A friend is quite nosey and asks you personal questions.

● People you socialise with regularly make sexist remarks.

● Your son arrives home very upset - his teacher had been absent and he had been absorbed into another class where the teacher had shouted at him and refused to let him go to the toilet.

● You want to return a bag of potatoes because some are rotten.

● It's well past your children's bedtime but they have just ignored you when you told them it was time for bed.

● You find smoking offensive but don't want to hurt the feelings of a friend who chain-smokes when (s)he comes to visit.

PLANNING FOR NEXT WEEK

Planning to do things you enjoy. *Below is a list of things you may like to do. As you read through it, tick anything that appeals to you that might be realistic. Add to the list if you like. Then underline three things you'd like to do more regularly - or begin to do. What will you do about one of them in the next 48 hours?*

Take a rest during the day. Walk in a park/by the sea/in the hills.. Take a lie-in at weekends. Watch TV/a video. Read a book about something that interests you - or a novel. Go for a cycle ride. Dance. Read a magazine/newspaper. Go to a film/play. Swim, perhaps once a week. Listen to music. Play a (board) game of...... Play an outdoor game of...... Enjoy a bath/shower. Plan an atmosphere for better sex. Meditate. Take a part-time job. Learn a new skill/musical instrument/language ...... Do some gardening. Go out for a meal. Have a special meal at home. Play with your children. Involve the children in your work. Make a new friend. Visit or invite a friend. Join a relaxation or keep-fit class. Practise relaxation methods regularly (like deep breathing). Plan a weekend break - and don't try to 'justify' it!

Talk in pairs about what you would like to do, what prevents you from doing it, how you could be assertive in this area - and what will help you to keep going. (During the week ahead you may also like to take some time to work through the 'goal-setting' in the appendix at the back of this book. It may help to ensure that you do make at least one change you want to make).

When will I take time each day to become aware and to foresee my behaviour?

_____

Which of the things from the list above am I going to enjoy doing this week?

_____

GETTING IN TOUCH SESSION SEVEN

WAYS OF CONTROLLING AGGRESSION

Here are some ways that help people to control their temper when they are feeling angry. The methods in the first section are temporary ones which might help you until you get the chance of the more total release that your body needs. A fuller release will leave you better able to control your anger when speaking to the person. You might put a tick beside any of these methods that have ever helped you, and an X beside those you would like to try.

TEMPORARY METHODS

1. Leave the room, saying 'I'm so angry I just need to go away and come back when I'm calmer.'

✓2. Remind yourself 'Losing my temper usually hurts people.'

✗3. Go and relax with deep breathing, music or something.

✓4. Go for a walk.

✓5. Talk to a friend/ partner about what happened.

✗6. Think of something completely different - to change your feelings.

✗7. Say to yourself 'I'm able to handle this without getting angry.'

✓8. Make some plans about where to go from here.

WAYS OF RELEASING THE ANGER

Don't worry about feeling stupid or ridiculous in a fuller release of anger - your body needs it. But choose somewhere private, like a bedroom with the door locked; do not expose children to violent emotions. Some of the methods below can be combined. For example, thumping a pillow or mattress in anger will sometimes lead to sobs, screams, tears. All the better.

1. Go to a bedroom, thump the mattress with your fist or a rolled-up newspaper, and say all you'd like to say, (out of hearing if possible).

2. Do something physical that requires strenuous effort (running, digging, swimming, cycling, cleaning..)

3. Have a good cry - tears can be a great release.

4. Twist a towel as if you were strangling it - and then bite into it!

5. Go where you can't be heard (a car with the windows closed, for example, if you have a car), and scream.

6. Write a letter to the person you're angry with, saying all you feel like saying; then tear it up.

SKILL PRACTICE SEVEN

This is a chance to revise and practise a variety of assertive skills. You're probably aware by now of some situations where you find it hard to be assertive, but it may help to look over the Case Studies from session seven. They should spark off some ideas for you and get you in touch with a situation to work at. Work on your own first and write down one or two situations where you'd like to be more assertive. Then choose one of them - but not something too difficult! Practise only with situations where you have a good chance of improving!

Now form groups of three, and decide who will be acting assertively, who the observer will be, and who the third person will be. Before acting it out, the 'assertive' person talks about what usually happens and what might be a better approach. If you're unsure, turn to Table Six and see what approach is suggested; then try that. After trying it, say how you feel you got on, and get feedback from the observer on body language, expression, tone of voice, etc., before moving on to another situation and switching roles.

If you feel the situation you choose may be either too difficult or too personal, avoid it. Just choose an easier and less personal example from the Case Studies and work on it.

PLANNING FOR THE FUTURE

There are two things you can do that will ensure that you develop your assertive skills.

1. The first is to find someone with whom you can sit down to talk out and then role-play before any difficult situation you have to deal with. It is useful if this friend is aware of assertive skills. Sometimes a husband or wife will be ideal; in other cases, they may be too closely involved with you to be helpful.

2. The second tip is to continue to take a little time each evening to relax your body and mind and become aware of how you have been using assertive skills. Ask yourself 'When today did I shrink from being honest and direct? When did I choose to speak up, or to be real, or to treat someone with respect? Then, foresee how you will act in one situation you will be meeting the following day. Notice how you normally act, and then see yourself acting assertively. This daily exercise can have a powerful effect in helping you make these skills your own in a natural way.

1. Who could I role-play with?_____

2. When could I take time each day to become aware and to foresee my behaviour?_____

3. Which methods in the 'Getting in Touch' section will I use for dealing with my anger?

_____

APPENDIX: EFFECTIVE PLANNING FOR CHANGE

Because assertiveness includes taking more control of our lives at home, at work, in our communities, the following exercise may prove well worth doing. It helps people to set written goals for achieving what they really want in life. Allow at least 30-40 minutes (or more!) to work through it. Write your answers, but bear in mind that some sections may not be relevant - answer only what seems to be appropriate.

1. What goal do you want to set for yourself? Wait - where does this fit into your overall priorities and goals in life? Why set goals that do not tie in with what is deeply important to you, especially your family life. If you do, they will cause unnecessary stress. So where does this fit into your overall goals in life? Is it a goal for your own improvement, or for your family, or for your work? Now, what is your goal?

Do you *really* want this? On a scale of 1-10, how deeply do you desire it? (The stronger your desire, the easier it will be to reach your goal).

2. What exactly is the situation at present? What is happening now? What are you unhappy about in this situation?

3. Don't aim too high. Set a goal which is an improvement on the present situation, but which has a good chance of success. Do you believe you can achieve your goal? If you are uncertain, lower your sights and write a more realistic goal.

4. What advantages or benefits will result from achieving this goal? Write down all the reasons why you want to achieve it.

(Writing down these reasons will make you more convinced of the need for it and will make you more likely to succeed. The more reasons you write, the more you will increase your own motivation).

5. Now the possibilities. What could you do to achieve the goal? Write anything that occurs to you.

6. Next the specifics. How will you begin? Where? When? Who with? Fix deadlines for starting, and mini-deadlines for the different stages:

Look at what you have written. Can you make it more specific? Are the details clear? Make changes if necessary.

Now write out your goal as a personal statement, just as if it was actually happening - and add words that will make it sound exciting,

e.g. 'I now enjoy......'

7. What do you need to achieve your goal? What information, materials, services, skills, etc.? Beside anything you write, make a note of how you will get it.

8. Who will support or encourage you? - colleagues, friends, family, experts, organisations, someone to share the workload, co-operate with you, free you up, give you information or encouragement. (You are more liable to do something if you tell another person what you intend to do!) Beside each name write *what* support they will give you, e.g. who will you tell your goal to, and who will you make yourself answerable to? When will you act on this, and how often?

What will you do in return for their co-operation? (Planning for this will prevent you from merely 'using' people, and it will also *make* them more co-operative). When will you do this?

What else will help you achieve your goal? List a number of ideas.

9. What will prevent you from making the necessary changes, or from achieving your goal? Include what has prevented you from making changes in the past, e.g. lack of discipline, loss of interest after a while; people will be critical; fear of failing; busy at something else... Write each obstacle on a separate line.

Which of these obstacles will be *most* likely to weaken or wreck your plan? Mark it with a cross. How will you deal with each of these obstacles, but especially with this biggest one?

10. What reward system can you build in to reinforce your plan? How will you reward yourself regularly and often for successfully keeping to your plan and achieving each stage of your goal? (e.g. I won't read the paper/ have a coffee until I have...)

When will you have reached your goal? How will you know you have reached it? And how will you celebrate, preferably with friends, when you finally reach the goal?

11. Set a time each day for 'visualisation', i.e. imagining actual situations in which you are achieving your plan. See yourself overcoming the obstacles, experience the good results, and remind yourself of your determination to see it all through to a successful conclusion - 'I will definitely not give up'.

(continued)

12. How often will you evaluate your plan? (daily? weekly? every two weeks?) Set a date now for the next time you will look over your plan, evaluating progress, and the obstacles you are meeting, and making any necessary changes to make the plan effective.

I will evaluate this plan next on...
Who will help you to evaluate?...

13. Now clarify. Look over your answers so far, and sum up the things you have to remember/ the activities you now have to do (including a regular review of the plan, which is essential). If necessary, number them in the order in which you will do them. Decide roughly how much time each will take, and when they will be done.

FURTHER READING

The following are just a few popular books on assertiveness. Some of them also contain lists of suggestions for further reading.

'Assert Yourself' by Gael Lindenfield. Publ Thorsons, London, 1986. Both a book and a self-help course on assertiveness. Includes exercises that could be done in a group as a follow-up to the present course.

'Assertion and how to train ourselves' Publ CETU, Halifax 1990. Ideas for a course on assertiveness that can be used by anyone who has gone through an assertion training. Well presented.

'A woman in your own right' by Anne Dickson. Publ Quartet Books, London, 1982. Addressed primarily to women, who have traditionally had less control of their lives, this book has many clear examples of assertiveness in action, and can be used as a do-it-yourself course by any individual (man or woman).

'Assertiveness at work' by Ken and Kate Back. Publ McGraw-Hill 1982. Good illustrations of how to handle many situations that are normally difficult or awkward.

'Assertion Training' by Deborah Clarke and Jacky Underwood. Publ. National Extension College, Cambridge. 1988. Very good on the thinking behind this type of course, what to watch out for - and how to look after yourself in the process.

GROUNDRULES

Those taking part in this programme tend to feel safer when the following groundrules are agreed right from the start.

1. **Take it seriously** You are asked to practise being assertive at least once each day during the course, and to take time each evening 1) to become aware of how you've been doing, and 2) to imagine yourself acting assertively in a situation you'll meet the following day. Regular practice between sessions is the key to success.

2. **No pressure** You have a right not to speak, and that right will always be respected - you will not, for example, be put under any pressure to do role-play in front of the group.

3. **Encourage others to speak** One of the best ways of encouraging others to speak is to give them good attention. You are also asked not to speak a second time about any topic until everyone has at least had an opportunity to speak once. One or two people hogging the conversation can spoil the course for others. Those who tend to talk a lot might draw others out and encourage them to talk first.

4. **Respect people's confidences** It is very important to respect people's trust and not to talk to anyone else about what you hear in the group.

5. **Start small** Don't start by tackling situations that are very difficult for you. It is important to build up your confidence by practising assertiveness in easier, simpler situations first. Starting small also means starting with yourself. The course is all about changing yourself - not your children, nor your partner, nor your in-laws, nor society at large.

6. **Beat discouragement** As you improve, you will sometimes have a 'bad' day, when you seem to go backwards. That is normal - everyone has off-days. Don't let yourself get discouraged or think you have failed, if you are slow about changing the habits of a lifetime.

7. **No preaching** The input for this course comes from this handbook and from the video - not from the leaders. So no one will be teaching you or giving you advice. But please show the same respect to the others in the group. They all have a right to their own approach and their own pace. What works for you may not work for them. So feel free to say what works for you but please don't offer advice or put any pressure on others to change.

8. **Question 'put downs'** You are asked to encourage and support each other in becoming more assertive. Also to support your group presenter by questioning any racist, sexist, or other remark that sounds to you abusive towards any person or group of people.

9. **Anything else** that would help you feel safer in the group?...

COMMUNITY PROGRAMMES FROM FAMILY CARING TRUST

PARENTING

'The Basic Parenting Programme'

This is a programme of eight weekly sessions that enables parents (of children aged 2-20) to improve their skills and create a framework of discipline and respect in their families.

It is the Trust's most popular programme and has been adopted by hundreds of community-based groups and by more than a thousand schools or parent-teacher groups (as an outreach to parents of children attending their schools).

The boxed kit includes 5 cassette tapes, 8 posters, 25 certificates, a leader's guide and one parent's handbook.

'The Teen Parenting Programme'

This course of six weekly sessions reinforces the same skills as the basic parenting programme while dealing with the more difficult situations met in the teen years. It is recommended, but not essential, that parents of teenagers experience the basic programme first, for this is an ideal follow-up to it.

The kit includes 4 cassette tapes, 6 posters, a Leader's Guide, and one parent's handbook.

MARRIAGE SUPPORT

'The Married Listening Programme'

Many initiatives offering marriage support meet a major stumbling block when they experience the difficulty of attracting husbands. This programme, however, offers four weekly sessions for groups of married women *without* their husbands, and the results are surprisingly positive — about 50% of husbands to date have been so pleased with the *effects* that have rubbed off on them that they have then become open to experiencing a course for couples. The programme can also be run for groups of husbands or groups of couples.

Again, this course reinforces similar skills to those of the parenting programmes, so it can be a good follow-up for parents who have attended a parenting course, many of whom are women anxious to involve their husbands in any case.

The boxed kit includes 2 cassette tapes, a participant's handbook, and 2 leader's guides (one for running single sex groups, and one for groups of couples).

SEX EDUCATION

'The Parenting and Sex Programme'

Possibly the best follow-up to a parenting course, and one that parents often express a need for. This five-session course enables parents to learn skills for talking and listening to their children (of all ages) about sex. It also looks at ways of dealing with difficult areas like dating, late-night discos, television viewing, peer pressure...

The kit includes a leader's guide and a parent's handbook.

ASSERTIVENESS

'The Assertiveness Programme — especially for parents'

A seven-session programme to learn basic assertive skills applied to the workplace or neighbourhood, but especially to family situations. An excellent way to complement the parenting programmes. Produced in co-operation with Barnardos.

The kit includes a Leader's Guide, a video cassette, and a participant's handbook.